SELLING SOLAR

YOUR COMPLETE GUIDE TO HIGH-PERFORMANCE SALES IN THE SOLAR POWER BUSINESS

DANIEL HOWSON

Selling Solar: Your Complete Guide to High-Performance Sales in the Solar Power Business

Daniel Howson

Published by: Selling Solar LLC

ISBN: 978-1-7367138-0-8

For further information, please contact the author at daniel@sellingsolar.net

For the future generations of solar energy professionals, advocates, and customers who believe in the power of the sun, and who will continue to carry the torch toward a civilization that lives in harmony with the natural environment.

In Memory of Jason Little.

One Love.

PREFACE

Transitioning to solar and renewable energy may be the most important change needed to achieve a truly sustainable global civilization. While sustainability trends are growing in popularity and gaining traction in every sector from food to fashion, there are limits to how much impact our individual choices actually make.

Sustainability trends are certainly worth celebrating. More and more people buy local and organic food, compost and recycle waste, eliminate single-use plastics, drive hybrid and electric vehicles, take public transit, walk and bike to work, and intentionally try to reduce their impact on the environment. While any of these actions reduce pollution, conserve natural resources, or help the environment, behind every decision we make to "be green" is one simple and indisputable truth: *everything requires electricity.*

Virtually every choice we make as consumers is influenced by electricity in some shape or form: the food we eat is processed by machines that run on electricity, kept cool by refrigeration that runs on electricity, and cooked with appliances that generate heat from electricity. The clothes we wear are stitched together with machines, displayed in stores lit up by fluorescent lighting, and cleaned by electric washers and dryers. Even thrown-out garbage goes to facilities that sort waste with machines that run on electricity, and recyclable materials are refined back into raw materials using heat from electricity. Electricity plays an essential role in almost everything we do and buy. This is just one reason adopting renewable energy can make a difference beyond our individual actions.

Even though electricity is a fundamental part of modern society, roughly one billion people lack reliable access to it. If providing electricity to the entire planet was simply a matter of generating enough of it, we would not be facing such a great challenge. Fossil fuel resources may only last us a few more centuries, but renewable energy sources are inexhaustible and virtually infinite. In fact, the sun provides more energy to the planet in one hour than is consumed worldwide in one year—making it a clean, cheaper, and more sustainable solution for meeting our future energy needs.

Electricity produced from renewable sources is no different than what is generated by coal, natural gas, or nuclear power plants. A light bulb doesn't discriminate between solar or coal. Once power is produced at a generation facility, it simply needs to be delivered to the customers who consume it. Fortunately, the systems we currently depend on to deliver power to customers can already carry electricity from renewable sources. The transition will require constructing new generation facilities and greatly increasing our energy storage capabilities, but it will not necessitate any major changes to our existing energy infrastructure or how we consume electricity. The fact that renewable energy can be seamlessly integrated into our energy supply without replacing any infrastructure is another reason it is vital to a more sustainable future.

Solar energy can be captured anywhere the sun shines, and for this reason, it can be installed almost anywhere. In addition, solar energy systems are feasible at virtually any scale, providing power to a single outlet or lightbulb or even an entire city. Because solar is possible at smaller scales, it relies less on other infrastructure such as roads and power lines that can be too expensive or challenging to build in certain places. Conventional power plants rely on roads, rail, and pipelines to perpetually deliver fuel, but renewable fuel is available wherever these facilities are built, which allows for more flexibility in development and scale. These are just more reasons renewable energy is essential for achieving sustainability.

There are many more reasons renewable energy is a better option for meeting global electricity demand, but we're not here to glorify solar. Renewable energy sources are "clean," but the fact that solar is a carbon-neutral alternative to conventional fuels doesn't make it a better source of electricity—it's simply icing on the cake.

Throughout my career in the solar power business, I have rarely met a homeowner who chooses to go solar because of the environmental benefits. Instead, the economic benefit (saving money), the prospect of controlling their electric bills, or the idea of energy independence tend to drive their decision.

In reality, solar energy is a workable solution for meeting global electricity demand because it is plentiful, accessible, scalable, and it meets a universal need: *everything requires electricity*. Developing renewable energy has its own challenges and environmental impacts while posing a threat to century-old mining, fossil fuel, and utility industries that employ millions of people worldwide. Renewable energy sources may not be perfect, but coal, natural gas, and conventional energy sources are anything but flawless. The bottom line is that millions of people pay *more* for electricity each year, while those installing solar panels are paying *less* than ever before.

Millions of people have yet to truly understand how solar works and how it stands to benefit them. The fact is that most people who learn about how solar works are homeowners who choose to sit down with a sales consultant. For this reason, the future of the solar industry is very much in the hands of solar energy sales professionals who are uniquely responsible for teaching future customers all about solar. Solar is ushering in a new era of clean, affordable energy and transforming the power sector as we know it.

Until going solar is as simple and easy as buying a car, a computer, or a cell phone, there will continue to be a huge need and growing opportunity for solar sales professionals. This book is necessary because it provides those joining this growing profession with the skills to accurately and honestly inform their future solar customers.

We have two primary goals: First, to teach future and existing solar energy professionals everything they need to know to build a successful career in solar. This includes learning the benefits of solar power and developing the skills and habits needed to sell to prospective customers effectively. The second goal is to raise the bar for the solar industry, establishing a high-quality culture, high integrity, and honest sales practices in the residential solar industry.

The solar industry is changing the world, and by reading all of this, you can become a big part of it, building the sales skills, deepening your knowledge, and preparing for a future **powered by the sun.**

CONTENTS

INTRODUCTION

Whether you already work in solar or are considering a career in it, what follows will help you *succeed* in the industry.

Chances are you've known about solar energy for a long time. Maybe as a kid in school, you put your thumb over the solar cell on your calculator to watch the numbers on the display fade away. Maybe you've seen solar panels going up on the rooftops in your neighborhood, driven past large fields of solar panels, or learned a bit about the subject in school. Maybe you are already working for a solar company, and you're looking to find an edge in your performance.

No matter how much you know, there is always more to learn. No matter how much experience you have in sales, there are always new challenges ahead. No matter what skills you have, there are always new ways to grow. And when it comes to solar, there are *always* more challenges ahead and new lessons to learn.

In the solar industry today, growth is the name of the game. After two decades of rapid expansion, professionals from all backgrounds are looking for ways into this exciting new sector. Since 2000, the United States' solar industry has grown by nearly fifty percent each year and added hundreds of thousands of new jobs. In theory, anybody can get a job in the industry but finding and maintaining success is a different story.

Selling Solar represents thousands of hours of work and experience overcoming obstacles for solar companies of various sizes, each with their own agendas and challenges. It compiles the lessons I have learned as a door-to-door lead generator, a sales consultant, a supervisor, a leader, a manager, and a pioneer for solar power in several markets around the country.

This book is not simply a "how-to" book, although you will learn the tools and methods you need to sell solar effectively. It's about achieving results and understanding what you are working for. It will be your guide to developing the skills, knowledge, and mindset that are equally important to leading a successful career in solar. I cannot teach you the patience, grit, and perseverance that it takes to succeed in solar, but I can teach you how to position yourself among the top performers in the solar industry.

Selling Solar demonstrates the belief that the future of the solar industry will no longer be driven by technology and policy. It will fall into the hands of professionals like you—the people who are working every day to galvanize solar into the foundation of our modern world.

The solar industry has often been called the "solar coaster," and sometimes, it seems like every week, changes are rippling through the industry. Every state in the U.S. and every country around the world has its own policies, prices, and agendas for solar power. When you have finished this book, you will understand how to navigate these differences.

It would be impossible to keep up with all of the changes in the solar industry, but one of the secrets to success that you will learn is how to adapt and persevere through constant change. These lessons are universal when it comes to succeeding in the solar industry, and they can be applied in any solar market, in any state, and even in other countries.

Simply getting a job in solar can be a challenge since most companies want to hire people with experience who will perform immediately. This presents a problem for young professionals starting their career and even those with decades of sales training who want to get into solar.

Newly hired employees may undergo intense training for a few days, a couple of weeks at most, but are inevitably expected to start performing shortly thereafter. Some companies are willing to wait a few months for their new employee's first sale, but are *you* willing to wait a few months for your first commission check?

After reading this book, you will have what it takes to start selling solar immediately. You will have the confidence to close your first sale within two weeks so you can receive a commission check by the end of your first month.

The quick rise of solar has attracted many people looking to catch the wave of growth, who expect their paycheck to follow the same upward curve. Inevitably, they find out that selling solar requires not only a unique skill set and some technical knowledge, but also strategy and commitment.

You can learn everything there is to know about panel efficiencies, equipment warranties, and production estimates. However, you will still find yourself struggling to find "the right answer" to a customer's question and competing against two or more other companies for a sale. This book will teach you how to remain calm and stand out amidst all the competition. You will learn to avoid the pitfalls of the dreaded "used car salesman" and to stop putting so much pressure on yourself and your prospective customers, which only creates more confusion in an already complicated sales process.

Developing bad habits is one reason why close rates for some consultants in the solar industry are less than 10 percent. Following these strategies, you will learn to develop good habits that will increase your close rate to 30 percent—or higher!

By the time you finish this book, you will know how solar works, and you will understand solar economics, policy, and technology. You will be prepared to evolve along with the solar industry, maintaining a strong belief in what you are selling and persevering through any volatility. Finally, you will develop the most important skills and habits you need to build deeper trust with customers, communicate clearly, stay focused, and ultimately sell more solar.

THE FUTURE OF THE SOLAR POWER INDUSTRY

In the first quarter of 2019, the United States completed its two-millionth solar installation, most of which are systems installed on residential rooftops. Many more homeowners are qualified to be one of the *next* two million installations. They will benefit from clean, reliable, and affordable electricity in their homes.

Most of your future customers have yet to install solar because they have not been properly introduced to its features and benefits. By reading this book, you are preparing to communicate these benefits effectively and learn how to overcome your customers' fears and uncertainties by providing them with clarity and solutions.

Millions of homeowners live in markets or utility territories where solar is not yet affordable or available. Whether this is because it is not economically viable or because local policies supporting solar aren't in place, these regions will be ready for solar someday soon. By reading this book, you are positioning yourself to be first in line to help millions of more people find their solar energy solution.

Many homeowners still believe that they have nothing to lose by doing nothing and continuing to pay their electric bill. The truth is that they have a lot to lose—tens of thousands of dollars at the very least! Until residential solar is more common and widely understood, the growth of the solar industry will continue to rely on solar sales consultants like you.

The power sector's transformation has been underway for the last few decades. As more homeowners choose to go solar, even utility companies are beginning to revise their development strategies by shifting capital away from fossil fuels and toward renewable energy. This is because renewable energy is proving to be a better investment, and there is a growing demand for cleaner and more sustainable energy sources. It will take many years, if not decades, for these changes to take place on a broad scale. The question for those who already qualify for solar is, "Why wait for the utility company to change?"

Millions of homeowners are seeking out better options and choosing to install their own residential solar and storage systems. They are choosing not to wait.

The world will continue to depend on electricity for the foreseeable future, creating millions of jobs and providing fuel for the growth of the global economy. The transition to a renewable energy-based economy will be primarily driven by finance and economics instead of the environmental benefits. As it happens, renewable energy will continue to allow us to meet our energy needs while minimizing damage to our health, the planet, and the natural resources we depend on—all the while creating *more* jobs and stimulating *more* economic growth.

Even Thomas Edison, who built one of the first coal-powered power plants, said, "I'd put my money on the sun and solar. What a source of power! I hope we don't have to wait until oil and coal run out before we tackle that."

So, the question is: Are *you* ready to put your money on solar?

Selling solar effectively will not happen because of knowledge or skill alone. In fact, your knowledge and skills are less important than the integrity, honesty, and emotion that you bring to each interaction with your future customers. The most successful sales professionals do not only sit atop the rankings because of their knowledge, but because of their ability to form relationships that are based on trust and emotion.

Throughout this book, we will focus on developing your personal approach to selling solar, relying more on your emotional and social strengths than your depth of knowledge of solar. In Part 1, as we embark on this journey together—whether it is to get you a job in solar, to take your career to the next level, or simply to teach you more about solar and sales—we will begin with a foundation of knowledge of solar that your career can be built upon.

BONUS FOR READERS OF SELLING SOLAR

THE FIVE CRITICAL STEPS FOR ENSURING A SUCCESSFUL CAREER IN THE SOLAR BUSINESS

Download your FREE copy here:

www.sellingsolar.net/bonus

PART 1

INTRODUCTION TO SOLAR POWER

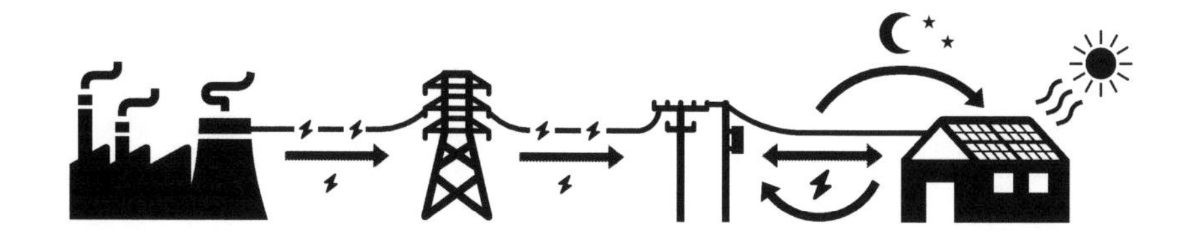

CHAPTER 1

A BRIEF HISTORY OF SOLAR POWER

In 2017, solar power became the third-largest source of renewable energy generation in the United States, surpassing biomass and establishing itself securely behind wind and hydropower. Solar is shaping the future of our energy systems, growing faster than any other source of new electricity generation, and outperforming projections even while facing sunsetting tax incentives and unfavorable trade policies. Solar is becoming commonplace in our modern world, but how many of us really understand how we harness the amazing power of the sun?

Solar sales professionals often spend too much time trying to learn everything they can about solar technology. The truth is that many of your future customer's eyes will glaze over as you explain the technical specifications of solar panels and how they generate electricity from electromagnetic radiation. In reality, selling is more emotional than logical, and your customers will respond to how confident you are about the future of solar, how clearly you relate the benefits of their situation, and how honest you are while working *with* them to find the best solution for their home.

The majority of successful selling is driven by an emotional connection with your customers, but the first step to selling solar confidently is understanding it. In Part 1, we will briefly explore the history of solar power, how it works, and the policies and business models that brought the industry to where it is today. Our goal in these next few chapters is to develop a solid foundation of knowledge before turning our focus to selling solar with confidence and integrity.

TWO TYPES OF SOLAR POWER TECHNOLOGY

In reality, the concept of solar power is quite simple: light traveling from the sun reaches the Earth's surface in the form of radiant energy, which can be collected and converted into electricity using *solar energy systems*. These systems fall into two categories depending on what form of energy—light or heat—they collect from the sun.

The first category is *solar thermal systems,* which use the sun's heat energy for a variety of applications that include space heating, hot water heating, and even producing electricity. Every time we step into the sunshine and feel its warmth, we experience the sun's thermal energy.

In fact, humans have been taking advantage of the sun's heat energy for thousands of years, which can be seen in the ruins at Colorado's Mesa Verde National Park that were built between 600 and 1300 CE. The residents of this ancient civilization constructed south-facing buildings under a large overhanging cliff that provided shade for their homes during the summer and took full advantage of the sun's thermal energy during the winter.

We will be focusing on the second category of solar energy technology known as *solar electric systems*. These technologies convert the electromagnetic energy in sunlight directly into electricity that we use to power our modern world. Unlike solar thermal systems that collect heat energy for various applications, solar electric systems are used for only one purpose: producing electricity.

THE HISTORY OF SOLAR PHOTOVOLTAICS (PV)

In 1839, a French physicist by the name of Alexander Becquerel was experimenting in his father's laboratory when he discovered that light could produce an electric current under certain circumstances.1 This phenomenon is that when a *semiconductor*—an element that naturally conducts electricity under certain conditions—is exposed to sunlight, it will generate an electrical current.

In the decades following this discovery, scientific research on light energy continued, and in 1883 an American inventor built the first functioning solar electric module. Charles Edgar Fritts' first attempt

---

1 U.S. Department of Energy, Energy Efficiency and Renewable Energy; "The History of Solar"; https://www1.eere.energy.gov/solar/pdfs/solar_timeline.pdf; (Accessed August 2020)

at a solar electric panel consisted of a large plate made of copper—a known *conductor* of electricity—using selenium as a semiconductor covered by a thin layer of gold leaf. At the time, Fritts had even suggested that his invention might someday compete with electricity generation from fossil fuels.

Not long after this invention, the first rooftop solar electric system was installed in New York—just fifty years after Becquerel's first demonstration of the effect that light has on semiconductors. Although Fritts had successfully built the first functioning *solar electric module*, the chemical properties of selenium limited its efficiency to just one percent. Ultimately, because of the limitations of selenium as a semiconductor and the high cost of gold, these early solar modules were not commercially viable.

The solar energy technology we use today is based on the early discoveries of Becquerel, Fritts, and many others. However, it was Albert Einstein's theories of subatomic particles and the photoelectric effect published in 1905 that finally provided the scientific framework for what we understand about solar electricity today. Einstein's discovery of photons (*photo-*) and the electric current, or voltage (*-voltaic*), produced by semiconductors under the right circumstances established proof of the *photovoltaic effect*, or the *PV effect.*[2]

The first solar electric modules were built using selenium, but following Einstein's discoveries, researchers began searching for more efficient semiconductors, materials, and methods for capturing light energy. Nearly a century after Becquerel discovered the PV effect,

---

2 National Renewable Energy Lab (NREL); "Solar Energy Basics"; July 25, 2014; http://www.nrel.gov/learning/re_solar.html; (Accessed August 2020)

scientists at Bell Telephone Laboratories did just that when they unveiled the modern photovoltaic *solar cell* in 1954.

What the scientists at Bell Labs in the 1950s had discovered is that silicon, an abundant element on earth's surface that makes up sand and quartz, is highly sensitive to light when it is refined into purified *silica oxide (SiO2)* crystals. Replacing selenium as the semiconductor, the first silicon-based solar cells achieved efficiencies between four and six percent, a significant improvement from earlier modules.3

Within ten years of this discovery, Bell Labs was producing solar cells made from silicon and licensing its new technology for commercial use. These early PV solar modules were available to the public, but the price of solar was still too high for most consumers. Due to the high cost of purifying silicon and manufacturing the modules, early solar applications were limited to government programs.

The first wave of growth in the solar industry was driven primarily by the government's appetite for solar cells. Solar became the standard source of power for all space satellites, and with federal support for the research and development of solar cells, their conversion efficiencies climbed to 14 percent. The federal interest in solar attracted more investment in research and development. However, despite the increased focus on the solar industry, high costs persisted through the 1960s when an important breakthrough was made by an unlikely player: Exxon.

---

3 Gray, Jeffrey L.; The Physics of the Solar Cell; Purdue University, West Lafayette, Indiana, USA; "Handbook of Photovoltaic Science and Engineering, Second Edition"; Edited by Antonio Luque and Steven Hegedus; 2011 John Wiley & Sons, Ltd. ISBN: 978-0-470-72169-8

DECREASING THE COST OF SOLAR POWER

The price of solar power has been decreasing for decades, following a steady downward trend marked by several rapid price drops. One of the main reasons why the price of solar power has dropped so rapidly is because of major breakthroughs in manufacturing solar equipment. In 2021, solar technology's price is still decreasing steadily, but this trend has been a long time coming.

When demand for fossil fuels was soaring into the 1970s, concerns about the United States' oil supply were growing. Oil companies were grappling with fuel shortages and facing the possibility that oil may become too expensive in the future, and as a result, they were encouraged to invest in research for alternative fuel sources—including renewable energy. One fateful result of this newfound interest in renewables was a chemist named Elliot Berman, who approached Exxon with a plan to build a solar panel that would be economically viable on Earth's surface—not just for use in space programs.

On his mission to develop an affordable solar cell, Berman determined that impurities in silicon crystals did not greatly affect the cell's efficiency. Using leftover silicon from the semiconductor industry, Berman reduced the cost of manufacturing solar cells from $100 to $20 per unit by avoiding the need to grow the highly purified *silicon wafers* that Bell Labs invented.[4]

Shortly after Berman's breakthrough, Exxon began manufacturing

---

4 National Public Radio (NPR); Andrea Hsu; "How Big Oil of the Past Helped Launch the Solar Industry of Today"; September 30, 2019; https://www.npr.org/2019/09/30/763844598/how-big-oil-of-the-past-helped-launch-the-solar-industry-of-today; (Accessed July 2020)

their own solar panels to provide electricity for water pumps at their oil wells around the world. As a result, Exxon's solar module became the first panel widely affordable for industrial and commercial use. The price of solar cells dropped by 80 percent practically overnight in the 1970s, and the trend has been continuing ever since—although not quite as drastically.

The price of manufacturing solar panels is just one of the many costs that factor into the overall price of going solar. Along with the price of hardware and equipment, known as *hard costs,* there are also *soft costs* that can amount to more than 50 percent of the price of a solar project. Soft costs include transportation, construction, permitting, inspections, and financing—not to mention marketing and the bottom-line costs of running a business.

Growing demand and the increasing popularity of solar over the last two decades has played a major role in reducing the cost of solar. As the market grows and demand for solar equipment rises, this leads to greater manufacturing efficiency and lower hard costs. In turn, installing more solar reduces some soft costs and operational expenses. As the solar industry grows, it not only results in lower manufacturing and installation costs but also attracts more investment.

Increasing awareness and demand for solar means that more consumers are considering an investment in solar. This, in turn, attracts the attention of investors, banks, and financial institutions who see the sector becoming less risky and are backing up the solar industry with more capital than ever before. As a result, the cost of capital in the solar industry is decreasing, and it's easier for solar businesses to get funding and solar customers to get financing—which is driving the overall cost of solar even lower.

Solar first became affordable in the 1970s, but demand did not increase rapidly enough to achieve the same *economy of scale* that is keeping prices down today. It wasn't until the early 2000s that a second wave of growth occurred in the solar industry, which has persisted ever since. This second wave was not driven by any rapid changes in technology or a major decrease in the price of solar technology, but instead by a different kind of catalyst: energy policy.

THE ORIGINS OF SOLAR ENERGY POLICY

So far, we have seen how solar technology evolved into its modern form and how the price of technology dropped significantly in just a few decades. But neither of these two trends had as much of an impact on the modern solar industry as the policies implemented at local, state, and federal levels, encouraging—and sometimes requiring—the development of renewable energy.

Concerns about energy security and the price of oil during the Energy Crises of the 1970s led to the development of modern PV solar cells. However, the increasing focus on the research and development of renewable energy technology was primarily driven by political action. Throughout the 1970s, the United States government passed several energy policies and created federal regulatory agencies that play a major role in the solar industry today.

At the onset of a national energy crisis, the Nixon Administration created "Project Independence," which called upon American science, technology, and industry to help achieve the goal of domestic energy independence by 1980.5 In addition to increasing domestic oil production, this federal program promoted energy conservation and the development of alternative energy resources, including renewables such as solar, wind, and geothermal.

Over the following three presidencies, federal energy policy would change forever. Gerald Ford passed five energy-related bills during his first few months in office, two of which were related to solar energy. A few years later, Jimmy Carter enacted two of the most important energy policies that the solar industry still depends on today. The first of these was the *Public Utilities Regulatory Policy Act (PURPA) of 1978*, which required utilities to purchase electricity from qualifying power generation facilities.

The PURPA legislation is intended to encourage the development of small renewable power plants, cogeneration power plants, and other qualifying facilities. Today, the policy guarantees that owners of solar power facilities may sell their electricity to utility companies with existing customers. This policy is important because it is the foundation for *net metering*, which is the backbone of the renewable energy industry today. We will discuss net metering in more detail later (Chapter 3).

The second of Ford's energy policies that would define the future of the solar energy industry was the *Energy Tax Act of 1978*. As a result of this bill, the *Solar Investment Tax Credit (ITC)* was created, which is perhaps the most significant and influential policy for the

---

5 U.S. Department of Energy (DOE); Roger Anders; "The Federal Energy Administration"; November 1980; https://www.energy.gov/sites/prod/files/FEA%20History.pdf; (Accesssed July 2020)

solar energy industry. The Investment Tax Credit has since provided unparalleled financial support to the solar industry, greatly reducing the overall cost for those who matter most: the customers.

The first solar ITC allowed an income tax credit to residential investors—capped at $2,500—for the cost of qualifying solar equipment.[6] Despite its limitations, the ITC nonetheless opened the door to public investment in solar and led to the first wave of installations on homes and businesses across the United States. The price of solar was still prohibitively high for the average homeowner, and those opposed to the policy argued that the incentives were ineffective and geared towards the wealthy.[7]

In 1978, the same year that the solar ITC was first established, a company in California called Real Goods Solar became the first business in the United States to create a retail solar sales division. After nearly a decade of concerns around domestic energy security, growing fears about environmental impacts from industrial activity, and the establishment of federal policies and incentives, the market for solar panels and equipment began taking shape.

Then came the 1980s.

By the early 1980s, the United States Strategic Petroleum Reserves were at an all-time high. President Carter abolished price controls on petroleum products, and as a result, the price of oil collapsed,

---

6 United States 95th Congress, 1977-1988; H.R. 5263 – Energy Tax Act; https://www.congress.gov/bill/95th-congress/house-bill/5263

7 Robert S. McIntyre, Lessons for Tax Reformers from the History of the Energy Tax Incentives in the Windfall Profit Tax Act of 1980, 22 B.C.L. Rev. 705, pp. 715 (1981)

greatly benefitting the industrialized economy of the United States. Meanwhile, comparatively high-priced alternative energy sources, such as solar, receded into the background once again.

Ronald Reagan took office in 1981, and his administration set out to unburden American businesses from federal regulations—including many of the policies and incentives that had recently been established in the energy sector. The Reagan administration removed solar panels installed on the White House and cut the budget for renewable energy research and development by 85 percent. As a result, the wind and solar industries were nearly wiped out.[8]

Almost all photovoltaic solar cells were manufactured in the United States until the Reagan-era budget cuts. As a result, Germany, Japan, and China quickly took the lead in developing solar energy equipment, and the United States has yet to catch back up.

The 1970s and 1980s were marked by constant change in the United States' federal energy policy. Following these two decades, legislative action on energy policy would slow down after Congress passed the last energy-related bill of the century with the *Energy Policy Act of 1992*. The ITC for commercial solar was extended once again, but the residential ITC did not make it into the bill.

By the mid-2000s, domestic oil production was declining, and the price of gasoline was increasing once again when President George W. Bush passed the first energy policy in thirteen years. The *Energy*

---

8 Perlin, John; "How Ronald Reagan Turned Out the Lights on Solar Power"; Updated June 14, 2017; https://psmag.com/environment/ronald-reagan-extinguished-solar-power-66874; (Accessed July 2020)

Policy Act of 2005 (EPAct) was written to launch a new energy strategy for the twenty-first century. The EPAct reintroduced the 30 percent solar ITC with an even more restrictive cap of $2,000. Unsurprisingly, the residential ITC was set to expire in 2007 before it was given a one-year extension by Congress.

In the wake of the 2008 financial crash, President Barack Obama presided over the passage of the *American Recovery and Reinvestment Act of 2009* (Recovery Act). The Recovery Act, part of a broad federal stimulus package, removed the cap on the ITC and widened the scope of the policy to include the entire cost of a solar installation, including engineering, construction, and permitting, in addition to qualifying equipment.9

The impact of the Recovery Act on the solar industry was two-fold. First, by removing the $2,000 cap on the residential ITC and expanding the legislation to the entire project cost of a solar PV installation, it effectively reduced the overall cost of solar by 30 percent. Second, the policy also solidified legislation allowing companies to receive a cash grant equal to 30 percent of the project cost on behalf of the customer. Although previous policies had set the stage, the Recovery Act was the game-changer that would transform the residential solar industry as a whole.

And so began the second wave of the solar industry. Developments in technology, price, and policy came together to create a perfect storm for solar power in the United States.

---

9 United States 111th Congress, 2009-2010; H.R. 1 – American Recovery and Reinvestment Act of 2009; Sec. 48 (a) (3) (A)

Pro-solar policies established in the early 2000s were emboldened by the Recovery Act, which helped minimize solar industry risk for investors and innovators. Local municipalities and utility companies all across the United States were emboldened to establish local and regional policies, tax credits, and other financial incentives to support the development of renewable energy further.

The demand for solar exploded, and as a result, more players joined the solar industry. More competition continued driving the cost of solar down and helped achieve higher efficiencies in manufacturing and installation. Perhaps most important for the homeowners who wanted to go solar, increasing demand led to establishing a new financing model that would bring solar within reach of millions.

Improvements in solar technology, the declining price of solar equipment, and the federal policies supporting the industry were the catalysts that the solar industry needed. In the mid-2000s, a brand-new solar business model evolved that spawned the birth of the modern solar industry, bringing solar to the mainstream market.

CHAPTER 2

SOLAR FINANCING: HOW SOLAR WENT MAINSTREAM

Solar power has been commercially available since the 1970s when the price of solar came within reach of both commercial and residential consumers. Developments in technology, price, and policy made this possible, but it was still not enough to bring solar to the mainstream market. It would be another forty years until the United States reached one million solar installations in 2016. Just three years later, the U.S. surpassed 2 million solar PV installations nationwide in the first quarter of 2019. How did solar reach the mainstream market so quickly?

This shift in the solar industry happened with the introduction of a new financing model that made solar available to millions of homeowners and not only those with enough cash to pay for it.

When the residential solar ITC was reintroduced in 2005, the cost of going solar still represented a major investment for the average homeowner. Anybody interested in taking advantage of the solar tax credit still had to pay for the entire project upfront, either by paying cash or taking out a private loan. While some could afford to invest the necessary capital, many were still unwilling to pay high interest rates on a loan—especially for a relatively new technology.

Installing solar panels is still a relatively large investment today, but because of innovative business models and a growing number of financing options, there are solutions for just about anybody. In this chapter, we will learn about a subject that will play a central role every time you present solar to a customer: financing.

As a solar sales professional, you will primarily be guiding your customers to choose the best financial solution. In reality, choosing how to pay for a solar PV installation is the biggest decision your customers will have to make. Until the homeowner feels comfortable with their financing options, they will not be ready to go solar, no matter how confident you are explaining why it is a good investment.

Helping homeowners go solar begins with understanding what financial options are available so you can work together to make the best choice. This chapter will explore the most popular business models and financing solutions available to residential solar customers.

THIRD-PARTY SOLAR, A.K.A. SOLAR AS A SERVICE

Around the time the residential ITC was reintroduced in 2005, a solar company called SunEdison was busy developing a creative new approach to financing solar projects. Their goal was to provide customers with a clear-cut option to reap the financial benefits of solar without investing large sums of capital into the project. SunEdison's solution, called *third-party ownership (TPO),* set a new course for the future of the solar industry[10]

At the core of the TPO business model is a common contract in the energy industry called a *power purchase agreement (PPA),* which utility companies use to purchase power from qualifying electric generation facilities (*see* PURPA). In 2004, SunEdison became the first company to adopt this financing structure specifically for the solar industry. Just two years later, the TPO model made its way to the residential solar market.

For the millions of homeowners who do not have thousands of dollars on hand to invest in solar, TPO provided a welcome alternative. By signing a PPA, the customer agrees to pay for the *electricity* generated by the solar equipment installed on their roof. In exchange, a third party pays for the *equipment* and installation, maintaining ownership of the PV system for the lifetime of the agreement—usually twenty years.

---

10 Kollins, Katherine; Speer, Bethany; Cory, Karlynn; "Solar PV Project Financing: Regulatory and Legislative Challenges for Third-Party PPA System Owners; National Renewable Energy Laboratory Technical Report NREL/TP-6A2-446723; February 2010; https://www.nrel.gov/docs/fy10osti/46723.pdf

In effect, PPA customers have a new electric service provider that offer TPO, or *solar-as-a-service.* The organizations that finance solar PV systems and maintain ownership are therefore called *solar services companies.*

The most obvious aspect of the PPA is that customers don't have to pay the high upfront cost to install solar panels on their homes. Beyond the primary appeal of solar-as-a-service—lower electricity costs without the high price tag—customers enjoy several services and benefits that solar service companies offer. Depending on how a customer chooses to finance their solar installation, the benefits differ greatly. We will explore the benefits of solar-as-a-service compared to other financing options later on (Chapter 5). In this chapter, we will learn how these financing tools actually work.

The standard length of a residential solar PPA is twenty years, over which time the homeowner pays a monthly solar bill covering the cost of electricity they generate. Over the course of the PPA, the homeowner eventually pays off the cost of the installation while they benefit from lowering their monthly electric bills—at the very least locking in a fixed electric rate.*

The amount that a solar-as-a-service customer pays each month correlates with how much electricity their solar panels generate. Traditional utility companies calculate electric bills by how much power a customer *consumes,* while solar-as-a-service companies charge customers for how much power the customer *produces.* Ideally,

---

* The term "fixed" can be misleading, because some companies will offer a low-upfront option that includes an annual escalation of their electric bill. For example, a customer's bill may be $100 per month in the first year, but increases every year by 2.5 percent. In this case, the customers electric bill will not be fixed, per se, but it will still be predictable.

homeowners want to produce as much electricity as they need but no more. Otherwise, they'll be paying for more electricity than they need.

For customers who go solar using a PPA, the financial benefits are fairly straightforward because they essentially get the same service that a utility company provides. Rather than paying utility bills for the power they need at ever-increasing rates, customers pay a solar service company a lower and often more predictable rate. Over time, the discount from this lower rate allows the customer to save thousands of dollars on their energy bills.

The introduction of solar-as-a-service in the mid-2000s led to rapid growth in the solar industry. As a result, the number of solar companies across the U.S. started growing rapidly—especially solar financiers. Customers with well-qualified homes in established solar markets could go solar without paying anything upfront, often reducing their monthly electric bills immediately.

The TPO model created unprecedented growth, and in the five years leading up to 2014, the residential solar industry grew by more than 700 percent.[11] At that time, nearly 75 percent of residential solar installations completed in the United States were owned by a third party.[12] Solar-as-a-service proved that millions of homeowners were ready for solar. They just needed a way to afford it.

---

11 Solar Energy industry Association (SEIA); Solar Investment Tax Credit (ITC) Fact Sheet; January 1, 2020 https://www.seia.org/sites/default/files/2020-01/SEIA-ITC-Fact-sheet-2020-Jan_1.pdf

12 Munsell, Mike; "72% of US Residential Solar Installed in 2014 Was Third-Party Owned"; July 29, 2015; Greentech Media https://www.greentechmedia.com/articles/read/72-of-us-residential-solar-installed-in-2014-was-third-party-owned#gs.6v42me (Accesssed August 2020)

Following the success of TPO, which is still a major part of the solar industry today, the rapid growth of the renewable energy sector sparked interest from more big players and a number of other options for financing solar projects. As a result, by 2021, just a few years after the dawn of TPO, solar-as-a-service has lost its edge to the other financial solutions that are now available.

THE SOLAR LEASE

The closest comparison to the PPA for the solar-as-a-service model is the *solar lease.* While many solar professionals refer to solar leases and PPAs interchangeably, these options are quite different in the details. While both the PPA and solar leases allow customers to install PV systems on their homes without the high upfront cost, there are several important distinctions between these two financial tools.

As we now know, a PPA transaction is an agreement to purchase *electricity* generated by solar panels installed on a customer's property. In this situation, the customer is not treated as the owner of the solar PV equipment. Instead, they are the recipient of a service that the owner of the system provides.

In contrast, a solar lease identifies the homeowner as the owner of the solar equipment installed on their home and enters an agreement to purchase *the equipment* installed on their property.

There are two common types of lease agreements, *operating leases* and *financial leases.* Operating leases are the most common type of lease—familiarly used for renting property or a personal automobile—providing customers (the *lessee*) with access to an asset that belongs to another owner. This may sound similar to a PPA, but in an operating lease, all financial risks and returns remain with the owner of the asset (the *lessor*). In addition, operating leases are typically short-term, such as a two-year car lease or one-year apartment lease, which does not work for solar payback periods, which are usually much longer. Therefore, solar leases are typically in the structure of a financial lease.

A financial lease is a contract that provides the lessee with the use of an asset in return for periodic payments over the lifetime of the asset. Financial leases are long-term agreements that typically result in the transfer of ownership to the lessee. In other words, the homeowner is treated as the owner of the asset, making monthly payments to take full ownership. Traditionally in a financial lease, the lessee receives the financial advantages related to the asset they are leasing, such as the tax advantages related to the asset's depreciation. However, the nature of a solar installation requires the owner of the system to make an upfront investment on behalf of the customer, which means that the solar ITC and any other incentives related to the solar installation will still belong to them. Because of this, not all states allow solar leases because of the potential for solar companies to take advantage of tax credits that would normally belong to the lessee.

Solar leases and PPAs share some similarities: both allow homeowners to install solar without the high upfront cost and provide long-term financial savings. In addition, many of the same benefits associated with the solar-as-a-service model are available to solar lessees. In other words, until a customer has paid off the cost of the PV system, the lessor will maintain responsibility for the performance of the PV system. The most important distinction to understand about the solar lease is how customers benefit financially.

By identifying the homeowner as the owner of the asset, a solar lease allows homeowners to make lease payments that build equity in their home instead of delivering checks to the utility company each month. The solar lease provides customers with low upfront options for owning a solar PV system while delivering some financial benefits that come from ownership.

Deciding between a solar lease and a PPA depends on a customer's preferences and financial goals—and whether these options are available to them. However, the introduction of solar-as-a-service led to an astonishing rate of growth in the solar industry. As a result, a new wave of solar financing options has been introduced that now greatly outperforms both PPAs and solar leases.

THE SOLAR LOAN

The advent of third-party ownership and the residential PPA led to remarkable growth in the solar industry, proving that solar power was ready for mainstream adoption. There is no denying the impact that TPO had on the renewable energy industry, transforming solar from a luxury for the rich to a must-have for middle-class homeowners with steadily increasing electric bills.

While PPAs and solar leases make a lot of sense for many customers, it is not always the most rewarding option. Homeowners are becoming increasingly aware and informed about the potential benefits of going solar—particularly the tax credits and incentives available nationally and locally. The demand for solar is increasing, and so is the number of people looking for the best option for their financial situation. As a result, homeowners are turning to financing options that allow them to maximize their benefits.

One of the less appealing features of the PPA is that the owner of the equipment is the beneficiary of all tax credits, incentives, and rebates. Some customers simply don't want to settle for the monthly savings from a PPA. They want to receive all of the financial incentives that come with their investment. In response, a new kind of financial option has appeared in the solar industry, *the solar loan.*

A growing number of organizations offer solar loans, particularly those focused specifically on solar and home improvement. In addition, many traditional banks and financial institutions are introducing solar-specific loans for both residential and commercial investments. But they are not alone. Many of the solar-as-a-service companies that previously focused on the PPA model are turning to solar loans as well.

By 2018, a little over ten years after the residential PPA was first introduced, solar loans outpaced TPO as the dominant financing solution for residential solar customers. Meanwhile, TPO reached its lowest share of the market since 2011.[13]

Solar loans not only provide short-term revenue for solar companies, but they also increase the value of local, regional, and federal

---

13 Pyper, Julia; "Solar Loans Emerg as the Dominant Residential Financing Product"; Greentech Media; November 14, 2018; https://www.greentechmedia.com/articles/read/solar-loans-are-now-the-dominant-financing-product#gs.8r6zv7 (Accesssed August 2020)

incentives for solar investments by delivering their benefits directly to solar customers instead of corporations. As with the PPA, solar loans still allow homeowners to install PV systems on their homes without the huge upfront costs. However, unlike TPO, the customers receive more of the tax benefits, rebates, and equity associated with the installation—as if they had purchased the system in cash.

The solar-as-a-service model is still an important part of the solar industry, although the solar loan is now the most popular financing mechanism in the residential solar industry. The PPA made it possible to avoid the upfront cost, and solar loans achieve the same but with additional benefits. In some cases, customers with enough cash to pay for solar upfront will still choose to finance their installation with a solar loan because they can keep cash in the bank or stock market while still saving thousands of dollars.

While the advent of the PPA and the growing number of competitive solar loan options available today mean there are solutions for nearly every customer, financing is not the only option. Naturally, any homeowner going solar wants to maximize the financial return of their investment. The best way to do that is to take full ownership of their solar project to receive all of the benefits.

THE CASH PURCHASE

Solar power has been available for residential customers since the 1970s, but until the mid-2000s, the only way a homeowner could go solar was by paying for the project upfront. The price of solar has decreased drastically since then, and innovative financing options have redefined the industry, but like any major purchase, cash is king. The simplest option a homeowner has when going solar is the *cash purchase.*

Early customers in the 1970s who could afford to install solar were not only motivated by lower bills and energy security during times of uncertainty and fluctuating prices, but also by the federal solar ITC. Paying for a solar installation meant saving money on utility costs and receiving a couple of thousand dollars through a federal income tax credit. When paying cash for solar is an option, it can be the most rewarding option for your customers.

Writing a hundred-dollar check to the electric company is not an ideal use of cash for anybody. The money spent each month to keep the lights on is certainly worth it, but everlasting utility payments create little additional value. Taking out a loan results in interest payments and more debt, but there are still obvious benefits: that hundred-dollar monthly check to the solar company is now building home equity *and* keeping the lights on. In addition, homeowners taking out a solar loan receive the ITC and other financial incentives available to them. For customers who choose to pay cash for their solar installation, their benefits are simply "all of the above."

Over time, monthly electric bill payments add up to tens of thousands of dollars. In addition, the hundred-dollar monthly payment will continue rising when considering the steadily increasing rates that utility companies charge customers. Considering how much money we spend on electricity each month, the possibility of eliminating this bill is appealing, but it requires a relatively significant upfront investment.

Purchasing a solar PV system in cash is, in some ways, like buying a personal power plant. Once it is paid for and installed, the system begins producing electricity, and the customer no longer has to pay the electric company for that power. Of course, like any power plant, there are still costs associated with being connected to the electric grid, so the utility company will continue to charge a *utility service fee* for the benefit of being grid-connected.

Several factors influence the return on an investment into solar. For cash customers, purchasing the system outright means receiving all of the incentives and benefits directly. As the owner of the solar PV system, the homeowner is responsible for maintaining the system and is motivated to ensure that it is performing properly. The homeowner has also improved the worth of their home by installing the valuable solar PV equipment. Finally, the homeowner is no longer paying electric bills for the electricity that the solar panels are offsetting. Each and every benefit goes to the homeowner who has paid cash for the solar PV system.

While payback periods may seem rather long in the solar industry, they are also relatively safe because there is virtually no chance that electricity costs will ever go down. Retail electricity rates may fluctuate annually and throughout the year but have been on the rise since the 1990s.[14] Any investment that stabilizes the cost of electricity for the foreseeable future is a good long-term investment. It may take a decade to break even, but the financial benefits will last at least three times longer.

---

14 Statista 2020, U.S. Energy Information Administration (EIA); "Average Retail Electricity Prices in the United States from 1990 to 2019" Monthly Energy Review, March 2020, Page 165; March 2020 (Accessed August 2020)

Going solar is a significant investment, comparable to the decision-making process of buying a house or a car. Whether purchasing in cash, leasing, or taking out a loan, most customers will base their decision on the overall cost and the funds they have available. Others may decide based on the features and benefits they will receive when going solar.

By 2020, just a few years after the dawn of solar-as-a-service, most solar customers are taking out loans to install solar on their homes. The price of solar is still decreasing steadily, so more and more customers can afford to pay for solar installations upfront. The solar market in the United States is continuously growing, and the future of the solar industry will be difficult to predict. However, we can be certain that technology, price, policy, and the evolution of solar business models will continue to be the most important factors. Any way you look at it, growing demand for solar means that homeowners and investors understand solar better than ever and are beginning to trust the technology more.

THE FUTURE OF THE MAINSTREAM SOLAR MARKET

There have been tremendous advancements in technology during the twenty-first century, and we have come to expect that major improvements are made every year. But solar technology does not follow the same advancement curve as computer microprocessors and information technology. Since the introduction of the first commercial PV solar cell in the 1950s, efficiencies have increased by roughly 57 percent—a far cry from Moore's Law, which states that processor speeds will double every eighteen months.

While solar technology improves incrementally, the efficiency of solar cells is steadily increasing, and there are no practical reasons this trend will cease any time soon. Solar cell efficiencies are improving at a slow and steady pace, but additional breakthroughs in solar technology and new applications will likely have a major impact on the solar industry around the world. Despite incremental growth in technology, the rest of the solar industry is expanding rapidly.

In 2020, renewable electricity generation grew to almost 30 percent of the global supply, including eight percent from solar and wind.[15] Solar still represents a small percentage of the global energy supply, but the International Energy Agency has estimated that reaching 27 percent by 2030 remains possible. Maturing solar technology along with large-scale solar applications, energy storage, and related developments in renewable energy is expanding the reach of solar power.

As the technology improves, it is also important that the cost of solar continues decreasing. This includes manufacturing PV modules and equipment, as well as the costs of developing, maintaining, and operating solar energy facilities. Even though the hard cost of solar has dropped so significantly, the industry's rapid growth would not have been possible without federal tax incentives for solar energy.

It is no overstatement to say that the residential solar ITC has been highly influential in the growth of the solar energy industry in the

---

15 IEA (2020), Global Energy Review 2020, IEA, Paris https://www.iea.org/reports/global-energy-review-2020 (Accessed August 2020)

United States. Since it was reinstated by the EPAct in 2005, the solar industry in the United States has grown by over 10,000 percent.[16] Policy will continue to play an important role in the future of the solar industry, but the fate of the residential ITC is unknown.

The 30 percent tax credit was last renewed in 2015 with the legislation including a scheduled phase-out of the residential tax credit. In 2020, the federal ITC fell to 26 percent and dropped again to 22 percent in 2021 before it is set to expire at the end of the year. This is not the first time the residential ITC has been set to expire, but unless congress passes another extension for the ITC or a new solar tax incentive bill is created, they will end in 2022 and beyond. Although the ITC has been instrumental in establishing a solid foundation for the solar energy market, the sunsetting incentive is unlikely to stop the growth of solar.

Federal policies can have detrimental effects on the solar industry. For example, the 30 percent tariff levied on imported solar modules in 2018. The roughly 5 percent increase in the cost of residential solar installations caused a moderate slowdown in sales across the country—but it did not last. The tariff on foreign-made solar modules was not enough to stifle the growth of the residential solar industry, which maintained year-over-year growth in 2018. In the nine months following the tariffs on imported solar panels, the result was effectively a $240 million tax paid by American consumers choosing to install solar panels.[17]

---

16 Solar Energy industry Association (SEIA); Solar Investment Tax Credit (ITC) Fact Sheet; January 1, 2020 https://www.seia.org/sites/default/files/2020-01/SEIA-ITC-Fact-sheet-2020-Jan_1.pdf

17 EnergySage Solar Marketplace Intel Report; Press Release September 26, 2018; https://www.energysage.com/press/energysage-marketplace-intel-report-7

As the residential solar industry prepares—once again—for a post-ITC world, we will likely continue to see innovative business models, advancing technologies, and new services like energy storage and management software define the future of the solar industry—and the overall energy landscape. As we saw with TPO, the major growth in the solar market has been driven largely by companies developing creative and business models and the increasing competition between major players in the solar industry. Looking ahead, as solar technology continues to evolve and the ITC expires, it is possible that the businesses that will carry the solar industry into the future have yet to be created or are now being built.

The solar industry is already responsible for billions of dollars of economic investment and growth in the United States, creating hundreds of thousands of jobs, and there is no sign that these trends cannot continue. In addition, private growth and public pressure are growing on utilities to switch to cleaner and more renewable fuels, exciting new technologies like energy storage and electric vehicles are reaching mainstream popularity, and the amount of investment in clean energy technology is increasing. In other words, the evolution of the solar industry is not complete.

Over the past century, the solar energy industry has been defined by breakthroughs in technology, business, and policy. Through all of the advancements and evolution, the underlying technology has remained the same. We may not be able to predict whether the same mechanisms that helped the United States reach two million solar installations will be the same ones that carry the industry to 4 million and beyond. However, we can expect that solar will continue to work in the same way: providing clean power for customers at a lower price than traditional electricity sources.

The outlook for the solar industry remains optimistic as solar technology becomes more effective, affordable, and accessible to homeowners than ever before. Higher rates of adoption may tell us that homeowners are starting to trust solar technology more. As a solar sales professional, it will be up to you to explain how solar actually works for them.

CHAPTER 3

HOW SOLAR WORKS

When we think of energy today, electricity is usually the first thing that comes to mind. This is probably because electricity is the most common form of energy we use. It is the reason we enjoy telephones, television, lighting, air-conditioning, electric motors, and it's used by almost all the necessities and luxuries of the modern world. Electricity has become so common that we simply refer to it as "power."

We depend on many important parts of the energy industry today, including the utility companies that deliver electricity, natural gas, water, and other luxuries to our homes to make our modern lives possible. Almost everyone has some experience paying a utility bill: writing a monthly check, setting up auto-payments online, or perhaps just landing on the "Electric Company" square during a game of *Monopoly*—the space on the classic board game is an astute observation of the unavoidable costs of utilities.

With the advent of residential solar, a modern version of the game would be prudent to include a "Renewable Energy Card" in the deck—the proverbial "Get out of Jail Free" card—that would allow the player in possession to avoid paying the electric company fee. In reality, solar power gives customers this option. So, how does going solar actually allow us to avoid paying the electric companies for the power we use?

In this chapter, we'll cover the basics of solar power to answer this question and build the foundation of knowledge needed to explain how solar power helps your future customers. The following lessons are not intended to make you an expert in solar power technology, but instead—since selling is primarily an emotional endeavor—to learn the most important aspects of "how solar works" so you can explain solar to your future customers clearly and concisely.

ELECTRIC GRID BASICS & NET METERING

If Thomas Edison were to appear today, he would easily recognize the systems he invented over a century ago. The network of power plants, power lines, and all the infrastructure that makes up our so-called modern electricity system is collectively referred to as the *electric grid*, or simply *the grid*. The electric grid is made up of three major components: generation, transmission, and distribution.

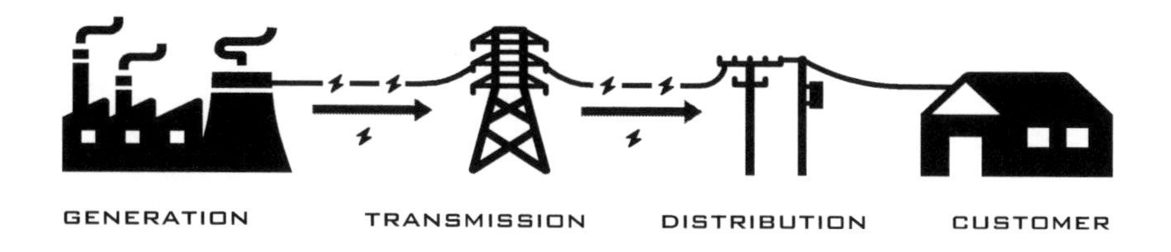

Fig. 1 Traditional Electricity Generation

Following the innovation of centralized power plants (generation), the modern electric grid began taking shape, designed to carry electricity from far-off power plants to population centers (transmission) and into the homes and businesses of customers who need it (distribution). This model of the electric grid—a sprawling web of power lines supplied by thousands of centralized fossil fuel power plants—is not the result of decades of planning and development, but an accumulation of systems that were built independently.

Utility companies are responsible not only for providing electricity to customers but also for maintaining the electric grid. As a result, retail electricity rates are determined both by the cost of generating electricity and the overhead costs and expenses associated with maintaining and improving the grid. Utilities try to keep prices low by supplying power from the cheapest source—historically natural gas and coal—but it is also becoming good practice to reduce spending on electric grid infrastructure. This is where solar power comes in.

Centralized power plants depend entirely on the electric grid, but solar power provides a cost-effective alternative to traditional energy sources. In particular, solar power is a *distributed energy resource (DER)* that could permanently upgrade the 150-year-old power grid. Simply put, DERs are power plants located on-site or near the consumers using the power that is being generated. For example, a customer installing solar panels can produce their own electricity right where they need it. Although this can reduce some of the stress on the electric grid, solar panels only generate electricity when the sun is shining, so solar customers are still connected to the electric grid.

The mechanism that allows solar customers to generate their own electricity during the day and make use of it at night, or when the sun isn't shining, is called *net metering*. As we can see in the illustration above, the flow of electricity on the traditional electric grid is one-directional. Electricity produced at centralized power plants is delivered to customers who are connected to the distribution grid.

Solar panels generate electricity when the sun is shining, but consumers are not always around to use the power while it is being produced. With net metering, the flow of electricity through the distribution grid becomes bi-directional. Any excess electricity generated by solar panels during the day is delivered back onto the distribution grid that nearby consumers can use. In effect, a new "power plant" has been connected to the electric grid that produces electricity during the daytime. The electricity that isn't used right away becomes part of the overall power supply.

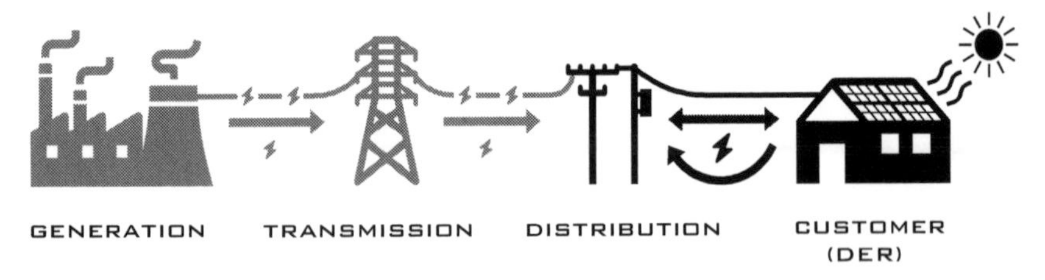

Fig.2 Distributed Solar Power

Net metering is essential for residential solar PV customers because it ensures that they get "credit" for the power they produce even if they don't use it right away. All of the excess electricity a customer generates goes into a *net metering bank*. At night, or in the winter when solar production is lower, solar customers draw from that bank as long as their *production* is greater than their *consumption*. When this happens, it looks very much like our original image of the electric grid:

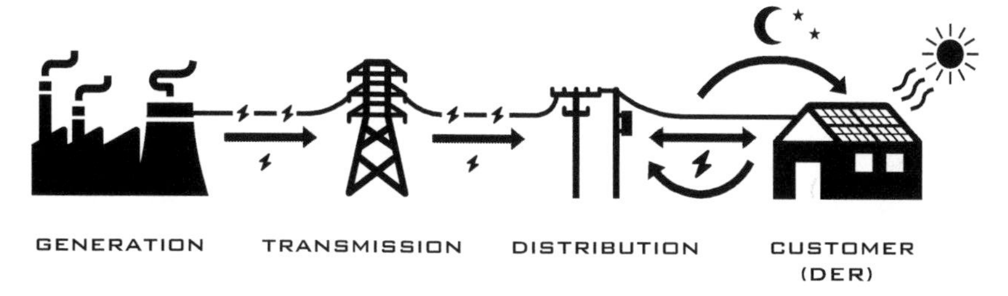

Fig.3 New Generation Model

Distributed generation is not a new concept, and solar power is one of many forms of DERs available today. However, solar is by far the most common option for small-scale, distributed electricity generation because it is safe, reliable, and perhaps most importantly, it is now affordable.

With a growing number of DERs, the utility company's role is evolving to be less about providing electricity and more about providing an energy management service. Distributed PV systems are essentially power plants located on a customer's property that generates electricity to meet some or all of the electricity demands on the property. When these systems are *grid-connected,* they are considered part of the overall power supply managed by utility companies. Excess electricity produced by a distributed PV system is delivered to the distribution grid and becomes available to other consumers connected to the same distribution network.

It is important to acknowledge that a shift toward a more distributed power supply will not make the electric grid obsolete. However, if the energy industry's future is to be distributed, the grid must become more than just a tool for carrying electricity. The electric grid of the future must incorporate systems for managing distributed resources, particularly renewable energy sources that—while inexhaustible—are not necessarily available around-the-clock.

One reason solar power is more popular than ever is that there are mandatory net metering policies in thirty-eight states as of this writing.18 In places without mandatory net metering rules, a growing number of utility companies are beginning to allow net metering. Other states have established their own methods for compensating distributed generation facilities. Without net metering and access to the electric grid, the benefits of residential solar become virtually unattainable. Net metering allows residential solar customers to meet their electricity needs by producing the power they need when it is available and using it when they need it. Put simply: net metering is the foundation of the residential solar industry.

HOW RESIDENTIAL SOLAR PV SYSTEMS WORK

Solar electric systems installed by homeowners to provide electricity to their home are classified as *residential solar*. There are many different applications of solar, but we will be focusing on how res-

---

18 Solar Energy Industries Association (SEIA); "Net Metering"; https://www.seia.org/initiatives/net-metering (Accessed December 2020)

idential property owners produce their own electricity by installing photovoltaic solar panels. Understanding how residential solar PV systems produce electricity won't just help us explain the benefits of solar power to customers. It will also provide us with a simplified look at how distributed energy resources supplement the electric grid while providing customers with otherwise unattainable independence from their utility company.

Residential solar PV systems are basically power plants located on a customer's property. These systems are made up of many parts, from the wires that carry electricity to the racking system that keeps the solar panels in place, but two specific components make it possible to convert electromagnetic energy from sunlight into the electricity that powers our modern lives.

The most important component of residential solar electric systems is the solar panels, also known as *solar modules*, that take advantage of the photovoltaic effect to create an electric current. A solar panel is made up of a number of the kind of photovoltaic *solar cells* that were invented by Bell Labs.

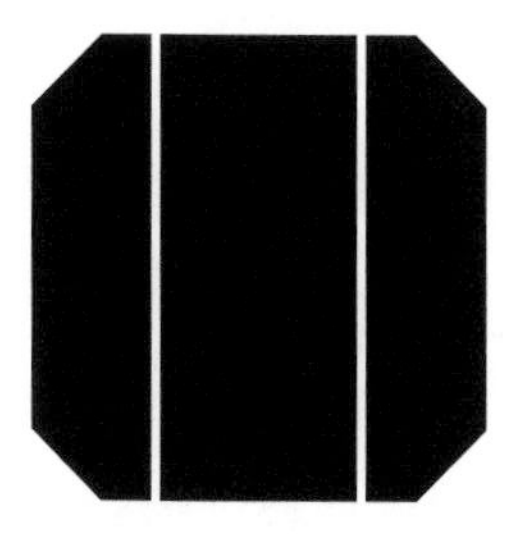

Fig.4 A Solar Cell

Each solar cell generates a small amount of electricity from the reactions taking place when they are exposed to sunlight, so by connecting several cells together, it becomes possible to produce more substantial amounts of electricity. Solar cells are configured in many different ways, as illustrated by the solar panel pictured below, with a functional surface area made up of sixty separate solar cells wired together in a series.

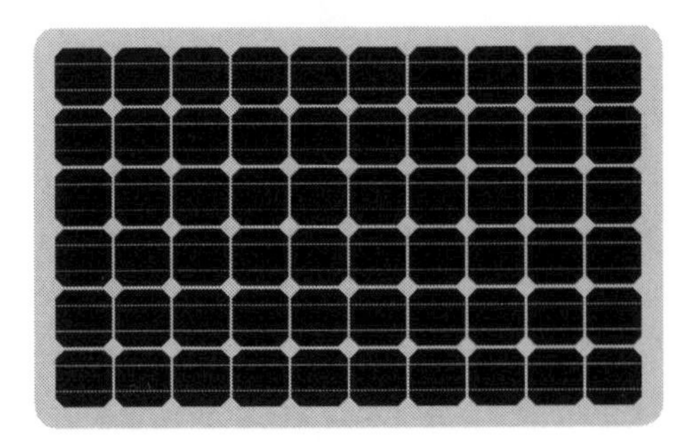

Fig.5 60-Cell Solar Module

The reactions occurring in each solar cell begin to add up when many cells are connected together, which results in more power production from a solar module. In a similar fashion, solar modules can be connected together to produce even larger quantities of power. When multiple solar panels are connected to each other, this is what we commonly refer to as a *solar array*, or simply a *PV system*.

There is no limit to how many solar panels can be connected together—nor is there a minimum. Solar arrays vary in size from just a handful of panels to tens of thousands depending on the application of the PV system—whether it is for residential, commercial, or utility-scale use. In the residential solar industry, the number of solar panels in a system will depend on a number of factors, including how much power the customer needs, how many panels can fit on their roof, and the size limits imposed by a utility's net metering policy.

The amount of electricity produced by PV systems depends entirely on the availability of sunlight and the efficiency of the solar panels being used. While we often consider how much power a solar array generates, it is also important to consider what kind of electricity it produces as that plays an important role in the movement or delivery. The second most important component required by all solar PV systems is the *inverter*, which converts the electricity generated by solar modules into a form of power that we use in our homes.

The flow of electricity is called a current, and there are two kinds of electrical movement that we encounter in our energy systems. The first is called *direct current* (DC), which is defined as a constant flow of electricity in one direction. The electrons in DC electricity are always traveling in the same direction. The second is called *alternating current* (AC), in which the charge will change directions, or "alternate," many times while providing a continuous flow of electricity. Both AC and DC electricity play an important role in our energy systems, and it is often necessary to convert electricity from one type to the other to meet our energy needs.

Solar panels generate DC electricity, so inverters are required in all solar projects to supply the AC electricity that dominates our energy systems. All solar PV systems have at least one inverter, but the number will depend on the size of the system and the type of inverter that is being used. As the size of a solar array increases, the number of inverters or the size of the inverter also grows. The most common of these are *central inverters*, or *string inverters*, which are placed centrally between a solar array (a *string of solar panels*) and the user or load. A second category of inverters, called *micro-inverters*, are attached to each solar panel.

Fig.6 String Inverter

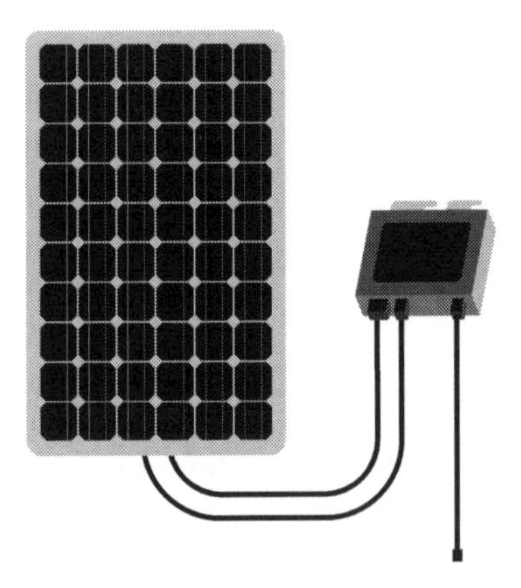

Fig.7 Micro-Inverter

Solar panels produce DC electricity from the sun's electromagnetic energy, and inverters convert that power into the AC electricity that we use to power our modern world. Just as it's important to install enough solar panels to meet our needs, it's also necessary to install inverters large enough to convert all of the electricity generated to avoid waste. As the size of a solar array increases, so does the inverter—or the number of micro-inverters—that convert DC electricity to AC electricity, which can be put to use immediately or delivered to the distribution grid where it becomes part of the local energy supply.

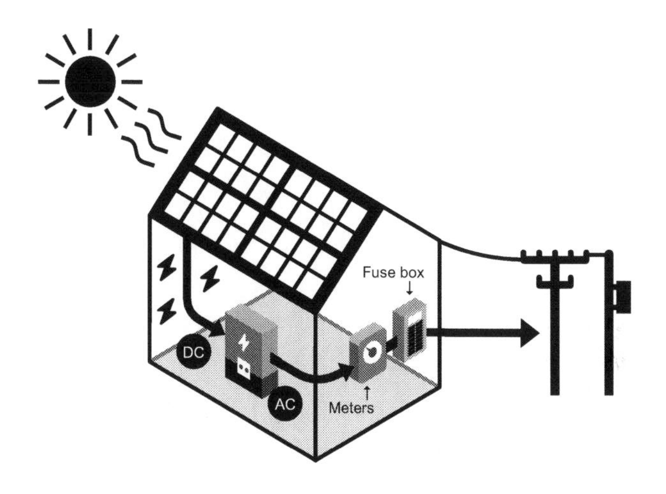

Fig.8 How PV Systems Work

Now that we understand the basics of a solar PV system—photovoltaic solar cells generate electricity that inverters make useful for consumers—let's look at how these systems actually work to offset the electric bills of homeowners and solar customers.

OFFSETTING ELECTRICITY BILLS

So far, we have learned about equipment (solar panels and inverters) needed to build a safe and effective residential solar PV array, and how the electricity produced by these systems can be delivered back to the grid and stored for later use (net metering). Now, it's time to examine how these two ingredients combine to meet a customer's electricity needs when and where it is needed, ultimately reducing their electric bills.

One of the most important concepts for calculating electric bills is a customer's *usage*, or *consumption,* which is used to describe how much electricity a customer consumes over a given period of time whether it is an hour, a day, a month, or a year. Each month, the utility company calculates a customer's usage—how much electricity a customer consumes—and charges them the applicable *retail rate*.

Usage differs each month as a customer's behavioral habits and schedules change, but these changes also follow seasonal trends. For example, during the summer, when air conditions are run frequently, monthly usage is typically the highest. During the winter, when gas-powered space heating is more common, monthly electric usage decreases. Every day any number of behavioral changes, from turning on the lights more in the winter when days are shorter or having the TV on longer for a sporting event, will have an impact on electricity usage. The best way to illustrate usage is by looking at the twelve-month history of a customer's energy consumption.

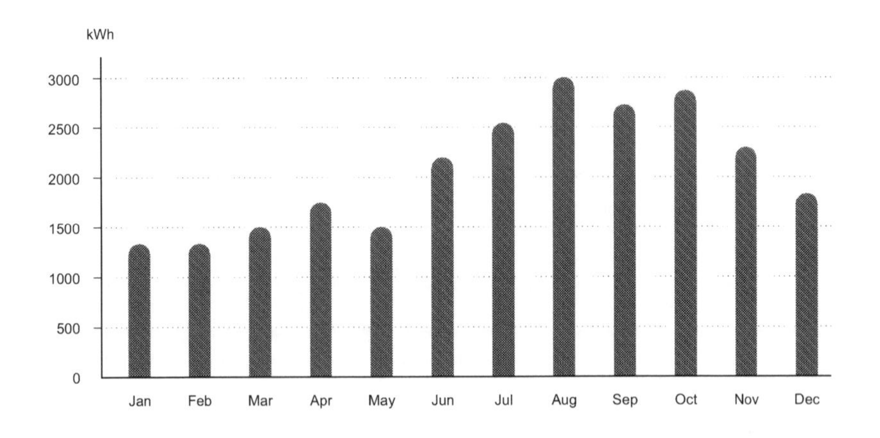

Fig 9. 12-Month Electricity Usage in Kilowatt Hours (kWh)

Utility companies bill their customers each month, so consumption can be tracked by looking at the amount of electricity used each month. It's most common to look at electricity consumption on a monthly basis, but usage can be drilled down by the day, the hour, and even into fifteen-minute intervals. The exact amount of electricity used is tracked by an *electric meter* at the customer's home, which the utility company uses to track consumption. The electric meter is another important component of the overall solar PV system, not because it produces electricity, but because it determines how much power is being produced.

A customer's electricity usage is not just used to calculate electric bills; it is an accurate predictor of their annual energy needs—*how much electricity do they use each year?* Even with behavioral and seasonal fluctuations in energy usage, consumption tends to stay relatively consistent year after year—barring any major life changes such as having kids, children moving out to college, home renovations, or changes in ownership of the home. Looking back at a customer's twelve-month consumption history, or their *historical usage*, is the most important figure for determining what size solar PV system is needed.

Electricity consumption is measured in *kilowatt-hours (kWh)*, which is the unit used by utility companies to calculate electric bills and an important reference point for determining how much electricity a customer uses. The electricity a solar PV system generates is also measured in kWh, which allows us to easily calculate how much solar power is needed to *offset* a customer's energy needs. Determining how much solar power is needed to offset a customer's electric bill is as simple as calculating how many kWh are consumed each year.

For example, imagine our customer, George, used a total of 12,000 kWh over the past twelve months. To offset his energy needs, we will need to install a solar PV system that generates 12,000 kWh each year. Assuming George has enough space on his roof to install a solar PV system that can meet this goal, he can completely offset the retail charges on his electric bills. As we learned above, George is still connected to his utility's distribution grid, so even by offsetting all of his power needs, he does not eliminate the need for the utility company and will continue to pay the service fee.

Continuing to pay the utility service fee can be frustrating for solar customers who want to go solar to distance themselves from their utility company. However, residential solar as we know it today would be virtually impossible without the electric grid and net metering—until battery storage options become as affordable as PV technology. To help our customers accept the utility's service fee, we can consider it a "net metering fee" that they will continue to pay as long as they rely on the grid to store the power they produce but don't use right away.

The careful balance between production and consumption is what allows both the utility and its customers to benefit from distributed solar resources. Residential solar PV systems can delay the utilities' need to pay for expensive grid maintenance and system upgrades, as well as reducing the amount of fuel that needs to be burned at centralized power plants when distributed solar PV systems are producing electricity—burning less fuel saves the utility more money. However, too much distributed solar can cause problems as well.

Most utility companies will limit the amount of solar a residential customer can install, typically to 120 percent of their historical usage. For instance, if George uses 12,000 kWh each year, he is only allowed to install a system that produces up to 14,400 kWh of electricity. It rarely makes sense for customers to install more power than they need—unless they anticipate some major life changes in the future.

While most U.S. states require net metering policies, not all utility companies are supportive of their customers going solar. There are many examples of utility companies—some successful—attempting to deter customers by charging higher service fees, introducing additional net metering charges, or even changing their rate structures to include exorbitant *demand charges* for grid-connected solar customers. Even in these cases, the financial benefits of solar outweigh the costs incurred by the utility, but these unfavorable policies further delay the rate of return for investments in solar.

HOW SOLAR SAVINGS ARE CALCULATED - PAYBACK PERIOD

Earlier, we covered the financial tools that made it possible for solar to reach mainstream consumers (Chapter 2). In addition to *how* a customer finances their solar project, the cost of electricity they are offsetting by going solar also plays a significant role in calculating their *payback period* and *rate of return.* The payback period for a solar PV project depends on a number of factors:

1. Incentives and rebates
2. Cost of electricity
3. Type of financing
4. Cost of installation

Depending on what incentives or rebates are available, such as the residential solar ITC or state tax credits, payback periods can vary greatly. As a solar sales professional, you will need to familiarize yourself with all of the incentives available in your market because each state and municipality can differ greatly.

For instance, if George lives in New York and decides to go solar in 2021, he will receive not only the 22 percent federal ITC but also a 25 percent state tax credit (capped at $5,000). If George pays $25,000 in cash for his solar installation, his total investment will be $14,500. In total, he has received a 42 percent incentive on the cost of his solar project, and as a result, his payback period is comparatively shorter.

To calculate George's payback period, the next piece of information we'll need is how much he pays for electricity. We know George uses 12,000 kWh of electricity each year, and if he's paying the NY state average of $0.18 per kWh, then we determine that he pays $180 per month. By installing a solar PV system that offsets all of his electricity needs—and paying for it in cash—George has completely eliminated his electric bills, aside from the electric service fee of $17, so his total monthly savings are $163. With all of this information, we can calculate George's payback period:

(TOTAL INVESTMENT - TAX INCENTIVES) / (ANNUAL SAVINGS) = PAYBACK PERIOD

($25,000 - $10,500) / ($1,956) = 7.4 YEARS

These back-of-the-napkin calculations give us a look at *how* we calculate the payback period for an investment in residential solar, but this is by no means an accurate depiction of the actual financial benefits. The calculations above assume that the price of electricity will remain flat and do not take into account the increasing rates imposed by utilities each year.* Even assuming the national average since 2000, a 2.8 percent annual rate increase cuts George's payback period by over a year.

George's financing decision for his PV system will also play a big role in his payback period. Customers who pay cash for their solar PV systems receive all of the tax credits, rebates, and incentives available—in addition to reducing or eliminating their electric bill. However, customers who finance their investments with a solar loan or a PPA will have an entirely different experience calculating their payback period.

Solar loan customers may eliminate their electric bill, but they are replacing it with solar loan payments, so their payback period is calculated differently. Customers who sign up for a PPA, paying little or nothing upfront and having no claim to the tax incentives and rebates, have an entirely different experience with their payback period. After all, if a PPA customer doesn't invest any capital upfront, there is no way to calculate a payback period. Financial incentives are a major factor in determining the financial *return* or financial *sav-*

---

* According to the U.S. Energy Administration's Short-Term Energy Outlook published in April 2020, residential electricity rates are expected to increase 2.8 percent nationally from 2020 to 2021 due to the increasing cost of natural gas. While we assume the national average here, retail rates will increase by over 7 percent in certain states and utility territories in 2021, information that is publicly available from your local utility company.

ings. As a solar sales professional, you will learn to use proposal software, pricing calculators, and other tools provided by the company you work for that make these complex calculations for you, providing a simple and easy way to describe the financial benefits for your customers.

Incentives and rebates, the price of electricity, and financial options all impact the financial benefits that solar customers receive. However, the final factor that is important to consider is the simplest: the price of the project. As the cost of solar technology, labor, construction, and grid connection become more affordable, the overall cost of going solar is decreasing. This trend is not only shortening payback periods for investors and making solar more affordable to a wider market, but it is also giving customers more flexibility in the decisions they make. Choosing the lowest-price bid is not always in the customer's best interest, but with such a high price tag for solar, it is often a major consideration for residential customers.

Customers who decide to save money on their initial investment, either by choosing a lower quality installer, less expensive equipment, or a smaller PV system, are usually foregoing long-term savings for upfront savings. Of course, a customer who receives two identical bids with the same equipment and production estimates with a $2,000 difference in price would be wise to choose the less expensive option—as long as the installer is trustworthy. However, the greatest benefits and the shortest payback periods are enjoyed when customers install the *right* solar PV system, not just the *cheapest* option.

At the end of the day, many factors are taken into account for solar customers choosing to install solar on their homes. Helping your customer understand how solar works is an important part of your job—from how the system itself works to how it saves them money. However, your mastery of this chapter's information will only contribute to a small percentage of your career as a sales professional. The most important key to your success will be learning how to tailor this information to your customer to work *with* them to find their best option.

In 2021, installing grid-connected residential solar PV systems is still the easiest and most rewarding option for customers looking for an alternative to paying monthly electric bills. As the solar sector continues to take off, there are sure to be more opportunities for customers to take advantage of this wonderful technology. While we may not be able to predict the next "big thing" to revolutionize the solar industry, we can prepare ourselves for the opportunities that lay ahead.

CHAPTER 4

CAREER OPPORTUNITIES IN THE SOLAR INDUSTRY

Usually, when the subject of solar comes up in conversation, the discussion is about the problems that renewable energy solves or its challenges. Developing solar power is an intriguing opportunity to meet the growing demand for electricity worldwide while reducing the cost of energy, preventing pollution, and decreasing carbon emissions. Developing new technology poses problems for existing infrastructure that will need to be updated and improved to incorporate a growing supply of renewable energy. In these conversations, we tend to overlook another category of opportunity that the growing solar industry creates: jobs.

The solar industry's future is dependent on technology, policy, and innovation, but also an experienced workforce. As confidence in solar technology grows, more customers are assured that solar can work for them, but it is up to skilled, experienced, and knowledgeable professionals to bring solar to these customers. This includes the marketers who find interested customers, the sales professionals who close the deals, the laborers who install the solar panels, and the many other positions that are vital for the global renewable energy industry.

In 2019, the National Solar Jobs Census found that nearly 350,000 workers in the United States spend at least some of their time on solar-related work. An earlier report from the International Renewable Energy Agency (IRENA) noted that over nine million people worldwide were employed in the renewable energy industry. This number could reach twenty-four million by 2030.[19] In the U.S., solar is deploying at such a fast pace that the Bureau of Labor Statistics estimates "solar PV installer" will be the fastest-growing job between 2018 and 2028.

There are many different jobs available in solar, from finance and policy to construction and installation, and each one is not only rewarding but necessary for the future of the industry. With so many potential positions and jobs available, how do you determine which one is right for you?

As you follow your career path in the solar industry, only you can

---

19 International Renewable Energy Agency (IRENA) 2017, Renewable Energy and Jobs - Annual Review 2017; International Energy Agency, Abu Dhabi; ISBN: 978-92-9260-027-3 (PDF)

determine what roles and disciplines interest you the most. No matter what experience or skills you bring to the table, there are opportunities for you in the solar industry. Engineers have changed course and led a successful career selling solar, and vice versa. This book focuses on a sales career path, a common entry point for many solar power professionals. In this chapter, we begin with the importance of *learning* your way into a solar power career.

STARTING AT THE BOTTOM

The solar industry is relatively young, particularly the residential sector, which began growing in earnest in the mid-2000s. With rapid growth across all sectors of the solar industry, there has been a similar increase in the number of new jobs opening for skilled workers and experienced solar professionals. However, since the solar industry is so young, most people applying for these jobs have little to no experience in solar energy.

Some technical skills, such as engineering and construction, are more transferable into the solar industry. However, sales and marketing experience is not always the tell-tale sign of a good candidate for a position in solar sales. Of course, sales and marketing professionals can succeed in solar, but there can be a steep learning curve coming from other industries. This creates a challenge throughout the solar industry because there is a major gap between relevant experience and job availability. The solar industry may be adding thousands of jobs every year, but the qualified workforce is still catching up.

As a hiring manager, one of the biggest challenges I face when hiring sales and marketing professionals into the solar industry is finding a balance between past experience and future abilities. The majority of candidates applying to solar sales jobs have little or no solar experience, so their willingness and ability to learn and adapt is often more important than experience. Professionals with many years of sales experience, whether in software, medical devices, or real estate, apply for a solar sales job without knowing the first thing about solar—let alone understanding how to sell it.

When I applied for my first job in the solar industry, I had just completed a master's degree focused on renewable energy policy. I knew I wanted to work in the solar industry, so I researched the best company around and applied for the door-to-door canvassing position.

At the end of the interview, the hiring manager was ready to offer me the job, but still seemed to question my ambition. He asked, "You have a master's degree in renewable energy policy. Are you sure you want to knock on doors?"

My reply was simple: "I may know a lot about solar technology and policy, but I don't know the first thing about selling it." I said, "If I want to sell solar someday, I had better get some practice. What better way than starting from the bottom?"

The solar industry was growing rapidly in Colorado when I took the job. At the time, it was attracting many experienced sales professionals looking to cash in on the growth. I watched many of them come and go, seeing little success. The ones who stayed shared one particular trait: they were willing to start with the basics.

THE DISCIPLINE OF LEAD GENERATION

To improve their performance, many sales professionals will begin to question their closing techniques and tactics. That is to say: they start at the end of the *sales cycle*. They think, "If I practice closing deals, I will sell more!" Of course, this may work for some, but no matter what industry you're in, the sales cycle doesn't begin when you close a sale—that is where it ends. In reality, the sales cycle begins when there are potential customers to work with. After all, how can you close a deal if there is nobody to sell to?

The first step to selling anything is finding a potential customer (a *sales lead*) who has expressed interest in the product or service you provide. In solar, lead generation is the most important step in the sales cycle. Whether you are beginning your career in solar, gunning for a promotion, or simply looking for an edge in your performance, there is no better place to start.

Since solar reached the mainstream market, general interest is growing, and more people are starting to look into solar on their own. As a result, some leads are easy to come by. However, connecting with potential customers who are curious about solar is just the first step since only one in four homeowners qualifies for solar. In the solar industry, finding customers means generating *qualified leads*—potential customers who meet all the requirements that will allow them to install solar on their homes.

Lead generation jobs are the most common entry-level positions, especially for sales organizations. These jobs entail a variety of activities, including going door-to-door, attending booths at events and retail stores, or even making phone calls to potential customers.

Lead generators are known by many names—field marketing associates, canvassers, event coordinators, customer acquisition specialists. No matter the job title, their primary goal is to prospect for customers and sign homeowners up for a sales appointment, the *solar consultation.*

Generating leads and setting appointments is the very first step in the sales cycle. Meeting with customers to sell them on solar is the second. Naturally, the better you are at overcoming the first barrier, the better you will be at successfully navigating the second. Generating leads takes time and a lot of energy, both physical and mental, but these activities will not only help develop a solid foundation of sales skills, they will also continue to bring in more customers throughout your career. The more you depend on others to generate leads for you, the more you are putting the success of your career in the hands of others.

Consultants with lead generation experience are more likely to become top sales performers. They have developed important foundational sales skills, patience, and the emotional intelligence needed to deal with potential solar customers, and they can go out and drum up more business whenever they need it. Lead generation is a skill that the top sales consultants continue to use throughout their careers.

Another reason generating leads is a valuable activity for sales professionals is because the first interaction a customer has with you or your company can be the deciding factor in who they choose to work with. Lead generators not only qualify potential customers, but they also set the tone for a customer's entire experience with solar. If you are the one generating leads and meeting with the customer to discuss their options, you have total control over the sales process and can better manage the customer's expectations and experience.

To illustrate this: if a new or poorly trained field marketer tells you customer, "You can go solar for free and save $50,000 on your electric bills," they are setting you up for a tough conversation. There are certainly situations where homeowners can go solar without paying anything upfront, and it's possible to save well over $50k. However, solar is never *free*, and financial savings depend on many factors that are nearly impossible to estimate without detailed information.

Lead generators may "only" be focused on generating leads and setting appointments, but it is still a critical step in the sales cycle that can make or break the success of a consultant. Your first lesson in becoming a high-performance sales professional is: *Success begins with lead generation.*

One of the qualities that most top-performing solar sales consultants share is that lead generation remains part of their repertoire throughout their careers. This does not mean you have to go door-to-door for the rest of your career, but rather you must stay involved in the lead generation process. You can develop your sales skills and develop your own pipeline of qualified leads with a few simple lead generation activities that we'll discuss in-depth later on (Chapter 15).

Generating a large volume of high-quality leads as a sales consultant doesn't always mean doing everything on your own. Whether the company you work for has its own lead generation budget, resources, or a team of lead generators, you can improve your chances of getting high probably sales leads by developing relationships with your lead generators, especially those who are most likely to generate leads for you.

Tag Along: Spend time with the lead generators on your team. Most of the time, the people in these entry-level positions want to learn more and improve their skills. Go out into the field to help train your lead generators, giving them tips and pointers on how to qualify customers and set better appointments.

Share Feedback: Make sure you are sharing feedback about leads and appointments that are being set by your lead generation team. Whether they are hearing it directly from you or their managers, it is important to reinforce positive habits and performance and communicate opportunities for improvement.

Lead generators typically get paid for setting appointments for sales consultants, while sales professionals get paid when those appointments turn into sales. The more appointments you close, the better off both you and your lead generators will be. If your team members learn how to set high-quality appointments with well-informed and qualified customers, you are both sure to see better close ratios—and spend less time with unqualified leads.

The relationship between lead generators and sales professionals is not always possible, especially over the last few years with the emergence of a new kind of solar company focused entirely on lead generation. These businesses function by generating leads through social media campaigns, online advertising, and other marketing strategies. Then, they sell the leads to companies or individuals who engage in the sales process.

These purchased leads can vary in quality—as well as price—and purchasing leads can be an effective strategy for some sales organizations. However, purchasing leads certainly creates distance between you, the sales consultant, and your potential customer. There is no doubt that the closer you are to the lead generation process—either generating them yourself or through a lead generator who knows you, your style, and knows how to set the right expectations—the better your chances of success.

When you can generate your own qualified leads, you will always have customers to sell to. And just like there are different ways to generate leads, there are different ways to sell solar.

INSIDE SALES OR OUTSIDE SALES?

One category of sales common in the solar industry is *inside sales*, which simply means that the sales representative helps customers from "inside" their office. This means selling solar remotely—over the phone and online—and taking customers through a virtual sales presentation. Selling solar over the phone can be more challenging than in person, but there are many advantages for both the company and the individual.

Inside sales allow for remote sales, which means that the company or the representative can sell solar in numerous markets while keeping overhead costs lower. For example, an inside sales representative in New York can help customers nearby in-state while also selling solar to homeowners in Texas and California. Inside sales teams allow companies to operate nationwide with a localized and streamlined sales department.

While inside sales departments are cost-effective, there are challenges to remote selling. Some customers prefer meeting sales representatives face-to-face and even the impeccable reputation of a solar company is not enough to overcome a customer's desire to work with a "local" company. One of the biggest benefits of inside sales organizations is that they can keep overhead costs low and therefore offer more competitive pricing. Remote sales teams can sell in numerous markets without the need for hiring sales representatives in many different states. Furthermore, with an inside sales team in a centralized office, the company's resources for training and development for that team should be much greater.

Deciding on what kind of sales job is best for you depends on personal preference and skill set. Before joining an inside sales team, make sure to consider a few important features of this model:

- **Advantages of Inside Sales:** Will you get more leads? Will you have more control over the sales process? Will you have better pricing than your competitors?
- **Behind the Scenes:** How does the company help you build trust with customers you'll never meet? Who installs the solar panels? Who will the customer interact with?
- **Additional Resources:** Are there more opportunities for training and development? Is there room for growth in the organization? What additional resources are available?

You must understand how any position can help you grow throughout your career. Inside sales teams are more likely to thrive in lead generation because customers are understandably more willing to commit to a forty-five-minute solar consultation than a $25,000 sales contract when speaking on the phone. Nevertheless, many inside sales consultants make multiple six-figure salaries because they know how to build trust, credibility, and focus on developing relationships with their customers over the phone.

Anybody can learn to close big-ticket sales over the phone, but this type of sales is not for everybody. Today, most solar sales organizations still focus primarily on selling solar face-to-face, meeting customers in their kitchens and living rooms, which is known as *outside sales.*

Compared to selling a product that customers are very familiar with—or at least understand—the solar sales cycle is often starting from scratch. Sales representatives have to sell solar to their customers, explain how solar works, why it works, and then navigate several other variables throughout the sales cycle. Because solar remains a relatively customized and complicated sales process, the in-person sales strategy is still the most effective.

Selling solar in person might be more effective because there are so many variables in the solar sales process, many of which are best addressed at a customer's home—such as looking at their roof to inspect the condition and discuss where the panels should go. Another reason is that PV systems last more than twenty-five years, so customers want to be sure they're making the right choice. Even though homeowners purchase their homes with a fifteen-year or thirty-year mortgage, the long-term commitment to solar tends to be a sticking point for some—*what if there's something better in ten years?* Whatever the reason that solar is best sold in person, there is one factor that cannot be overlooked: trust.

Solar represents a big investment, a long-term commitment, and it's based on a relatively new and unfamiliar technology. To sell solar effectively, consultants must gain the trust of their customers. As a solar sales professional, the single-most-important part of your job will be building trust with your customers.

Outside sales consultants build relationships with their customers in person—at their kitchen table, in their living room, or wherever you meet with them—as well as communicating and following up through email and over the phone. While inside sales professionals rely entirely on phone and email communication, outside sales consultants have the advantage of using that and everything else.

Both inside sales and outside sales organizations have their advantages and disadvantages. A solar sales professional's most important choice is deciding a company structure that works best for their skills and personality, as well as other considerations that make one choice better than others. While there are no right or wrong choices, your second lesson in becoming a top sales professional is: *Choose the right path for you.*

As a solar sales professional, you are not only responsible for providing compelling presentations to your customers. You will also represent the solar industry as a whole. In such a young and exciting industry saving money may bring customers to you, but the experience that you provide your customers—one that is driven by honesty and integrity—will be the reason they choose to go solar with you.

Most homeowners looking into solar for the first time have to believe a lot of things that solar sales professionals are telling them:

- **The Benefits –** The potential financial savings: how much are they *really* going to save by going solar?
- **The Cost –** The price of installing solar: how much are they *really* investing when all is said and done?
- **The Expectation –** The impact solar will have on their home: how much are they *really* going to deal with this equipment on their roof?

In a perfect world, homeowners would do their own research to confirm the benefits of solar, but in most cases, they choose to believe the sales professionals. For this reason, it is up to solar sales consultants to provide accurate information and focus on making a good name for the solar industry. This doesn't just mean being honest and transparent about what you're offering to customers, but also taking responsibility to ensure that you are working for the right kind of solar company—one that puts quality and integrity in front of profit.

Your best chances of success as a solar sales professional will be working for a solar company with a track record of high-quality installations and good customer relationships, not just the lowest prices around. The company you work for can affect your ability to sell effectively, and lower prices don't always lead to more sales. In fact, lower prices usually mean your commission checks will be smaller.

In the highly competitive solar industry, lower prices usually indicate lower quality installations or equipment—or both—which rarely lead to happy customers willing to give positive reviews or refer their family, friends, and neighbors.

Many solar companies find a good balance between price and quality, offering competitive prices to customers willing to pay a little extra for a better product and experience. It's not always enough to read reviews about the company you choose to work for. There are ways to falsify positive reviews and sweep bad ones under the rug.

Any solar company with honest reviews that wants to hire you should be willing to produce evidence of happy customers—and even unhappy ones. Before you choose to work for any solar company, you should see the quality of their work first hand and see how they deal with unsatisfactory customer experiences.

As an outside sales consultant, you will spend a lot of time in your future customers' homes explaining the benefits of going solar. When you finish your presentation, the customer will have two decisions to make. First, they will need to decide whether or not it makes sense to go solar. Second, they will have to decide who to work with. Forming a relationship with your customers built on trust, honesty, integrity, and quality might not be enough to overcome a $10,000 difference between you and your competitors, but this is rarely the case in the solar industry. Your customers will choose to work with you because they believe in you, even if it means the difference of a few thousand dollars.

When you believe in the product you are selling, your customers will believe in your product. When you believe in the company you work for, your customers will believe in your company. Your third lesson in becoming a successful solar sales consultant is: *Never underestimate the importance of trust—choose the right company.*

The subjects we have covered in the first part of this book are important parts of a foundation for a successful career selling solar. Understanding the history of this fast-growing market builds confidence—knowing what financial mechanisms helped millions of homeowners go solar provides context, learning how solar works builds knowledge, and pursuing the right opportunities ensures personal harmony. Although your success will depend on confidence, context, knowledge, and harmony, the path to becoming a top-performing sales professional is paved with trust, honesty, and integrity.

In Part 2, we will dive into the features and benefits of solar that are attracting homeowners and improving the lives of millions. The features customers experience depend on their choices, and the benefits they receive depend on their qualifications. However, their overall experience will depend on how you choose to present solar to them. In the following chapters, you will learn about the features and benefits of solar and the qualities that make a good candidate for solar. As a solar sales professional, your ability to be honest, straightforward, and accurate when qualifying customers and explaining these features and benefits will greatly impact your success. It will also guide you to waste less time and save your energy for the most qualified customers who will most likely go solar.

PART 2

THE FEATURES AND BENEFITS OF SOLAR POWER

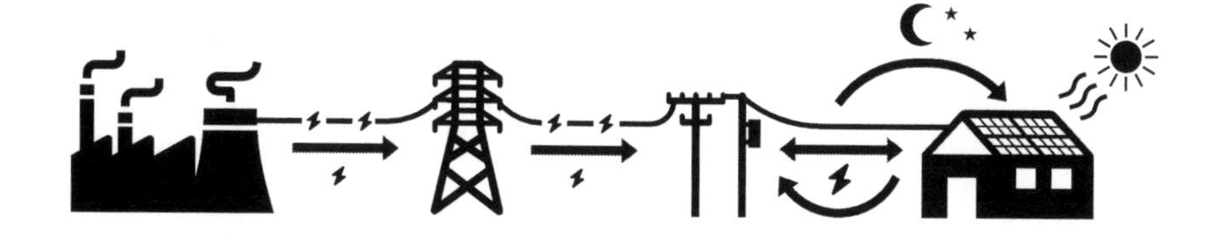

CHAPTER 5

THE FINANCIAL BENEFITS OF SOLAR POWER

Working in the solar industry is guaranteed to be interesting and ever-changing. There have been so many ups and downs that it is common to hear the industry referred to as the "solar coaster." However, with all of the changes and developments in policy, technology, price, and financing, there is perhaps one thing in the solar industry that remains constant: *the benefits.*

There are many choices a solar customer must make when deciding to install solar panels, from the size of the system to the design of the installation to the type of equipment used. With all of these choices taken into consideration, how do these decisions affect the benefits that the customer receives from solar?

In this chapter, we will begin exploring the features and benefits that customers may experience when they install solar panels on their homes. Not all customers will experience each one of the following features and benefits because of various factors, including how they choose to finance their solar project, how much electricity they can offset with solar, the material their roof is made of, and so on. However, the following features and benefits are important to understand and will come into play at some point in your sales career.

At the end of the day, it will be up to you—the solar sales consultant—to determine which of these features and benefits are most appealing and most important to your customer. You will be responsible for explaining how these benefits relate to them individually, and in some cases, why they *won't* receive some benefits.

To make things a little easier, we will separate the features and benefits of solar into three categories covered in the following chapters: financial benefits, service benefits, and environmental benefits. The financial and service-based benefits of solar are experience directly by customers, while the environmental benefits of solar are considered to be *positive externalities*.

THE FINANCIAL BENEFITS OF SOLAR

We have already discussed the various financial choices that homeowners have when going solar (Chapter 2). By now, it should be clear that depending on how you pay for a solar installation, the incentives, savings, payback period, and overall experience will vary greatly. However, no matter how customers go solar, they will be experiencing the same thing: saving money by generating their own electricity at a lower rate than the utility company.

Financial Benefit #1: Electric Bill Savings.

The number one reason homeowners decide to install solar is the financial benefit, or simply to save money. While *eliminating* their electric bill is not always possible, going solar allows customers to spend less money on electricity by *lowering* their cost of power. The first and foremost benefit of going solar are *electric bill savings.*

To illustrate electric bill savings, let's consider an example customer, Elizabeth, who had a $200 electric utility bill until she installed enough solar power to offset 80 percent of her monthly electricity consumption. As a result, her utility bill is reduced to $40 per month, and the rest of her electricity comes from the solar panels on her roof. Electric bill savings are calculated by the formula:

OLD UTILITY BILL - NEW UTILITY BILL = SOLAR SAVINGS

Elizabeth's electric bill savings can be described monthly: she is spending $160 less on utility payments each month. Or annually: she will be saving nearly $2,000 on her electric bills in the first year after her system is installed. She may still be paying the utility, but her overall cost of electricity is now 80 percent lower because she is producing most of her own power instead of buying from the electric company.

The electric bill savings is *the benefit a customer receives by lowering the amount of money they pay for electricity.*

Financial Benefit #2: Avoided Cost of Power.

Since 2010, residential electricity rates in the United States have increased by roughly 15 percent, according to data from the U.S. Energy Information Administration. In some years, utility rates have risen by over 10 percent, and in some regions, rates have jumped by nearly 12 percent in a single year, a much faster rate than the national average.[20] To help determine the financial benefits of going solar, we have to take into consideration the "cost of doing nothing," or what we call the *avoided cost of power.*

Determining the avoided cost of power is one of the more complicated calculations that we use to understand financial benefits, but it is critical to calculating financial returns. Returning to our customer, Elizabeth, let's imagine that her utility company currently charges her $0.25 per kWh and raises rates by 4 percent each year. If Elizabeth "does nothing," she will be paying about $0.26 per kWh for the same electricity next year, and in five years, her bills will be 22 percent higher than they are today. In twenty years, Elizabeth will be paying $0.53 per kWh, a 119 percent increase from today.

The avoided cost of power is so important to understand because even though Elizabeth's $200 electric bill seems manageable today, soon she will be paying over $300 if she chooses to do nothing about it. On average, Elizabeth's electric rate will be $0.39 per kWh over the next twenty years, or 55 percent higher than what she currently pays.

---

20 U.S. Energy Information Agency, August 2014; *Electric Power Monthly; https://www.eia.gov/todayinenergy/detail.php?id=17791*

By choosing to go solar, Elizabeth is not only reducing her electric bills (benefit number one), she is also *avoiding* the inevitable higher prices in the future. Learning how to calculate the avoided cost of power is unnecessary because solar proposal tools calculate these figures for you. However, knowing how to explain this benefit to your customers will be one of your greatest tools.

The price of installing a solar PV system can be calculated in the same way as a $/kWh price. If we assume that it costs Elizabeth $0.25 per kWh to install her solar PV system—the same price she currently pays for electricity from her utility—we can calculate the avoided cost of power accordingly. Over twenty years, the simplified avoided cost of power is calculated by the formula:

COST OF PAYING FOR UTILITY POWER - COST OF GOING SOLAR = SIMPLIFIED AVOIDED COST OF POWER

In our example with Elizabeth, this means:

$0.39 (AVG. 20-YEAR COST/KWH) - $0.25 (COST OF INSTALLING SOLAR) = $0.14 / KWH

Put simply, when Elizabeth chooses to go solar, she is saving a minimum of $0.14 per kWh over the next twenty years, which means she will avoid having to pay the utility company $33,600 for electricity.

Although we are calculating these numbers in simplified terms, the real-world applications also incorporate other factors that contribute to the avoided cost of power, such as state and federal tax incentives. The avoided cost of power will vary significantly depending on utility prices, the rate that utility rates are increasing, the cost of solar, and of course, how the customer pays for their PV installation. While you could use all these variables to calculate the avoided cost of power for a specific customer, the solar proposal software you use to create proposals for your customers will generate these figures for you. Rather than learning how to calculate this number, your time will be better spent learning how to help customers understand why this number is important.

The avoided cost of power is *the benefit a customer receives by avoiding the increasing rate utilities charge for electricity.*

Financial Benefit #3: Predictable Electric Bills.

The previous two benefits are both financial, but they are also based on particular numbers or calculations specific to a customer. One financial benefit that is not necessarily determined by a formula is predictability. The value of financial control is overlooked in many ways, but in reality, this is one of the most effective selling points for solar.

Utility bills will inevitably differ each month, which represents a variable and unpredictable financial responsibility for utility customers. It is almost impossible to know exactly how much your electric bill will be at the end of any given month—let alone in the years to come. You already learned that this is because electricity consumption differs depending on how much power customers use, such as their lights, televisions, air conditioners, or any electric appliances (Chapter 3). Electric bills are affected by family members visiting, friends coming over for a party, or if you go out of town for a week. By going solar, customers not only reduce their energy spending but take control of how much they spend each month.

To illustrate this, let's meet another example customer, Edward, who installed a solar PV system on his roof that produces 100 percent of the electricity he needs. Before Edward went solar, he was paying an average of $200 per month to his utility company, but after taking out a solar loan, his monthly electric bill—his solar loan payments—are exactly $170 per month. While we know that Edward previously paid an average of $200 per month for electricity, in reality, his monthly electric bills can look something like this:

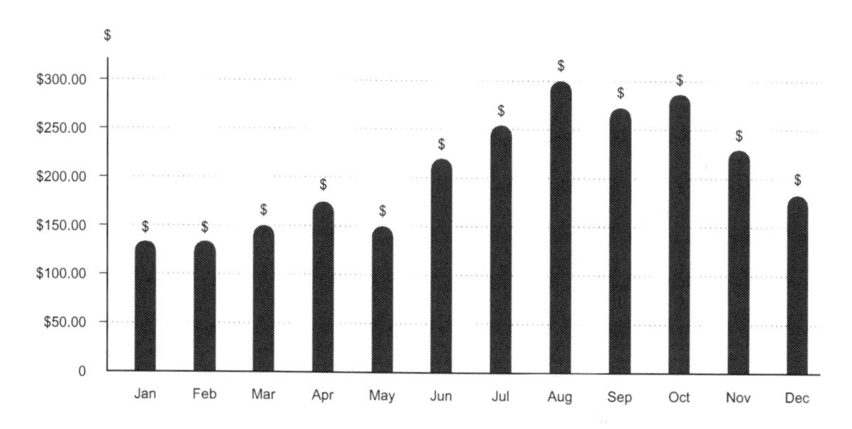

Fig 10. Monthly Electric Bills ($)

Edward's average electric bill may sound reasonable, at $200 per month, but from August to October, he is paying nearly $300 to his utility company. Such high bills can have a serious impact on monthly budgets—especially cash that would be better spent on back-to-school shopping, Labor Day activities, or other more worthwhile investments.

Once Edward's solar panels start producing electricity, his monthly electric bills are not only lower, but he also knows exactly how much he needs to set aside for electricity each month. This is what we mean when we say, "Take control of your electric bills." When customers know exactly how much their solar bill will be each month, they can establish more predictable budgets and put the savings they get from solar into more worthwhile investments.

Having more predictable electric bills is *a benefit the customer receives knowing how much they will be spending on electricity each month.*

Financial Benefit #4: Improving Home Value.

There's no hiding the fact that going solar represents a major investment for the average person. In addition to the high price tag, the financial benefits from going solar can be vague and difficult to understand. However, homeowners who choose to do so are not only setting themselves up to benefit from the savings, avoided costs, and predictability of solar. They are also investing in an asset that allows them to build equity in their home.

In some ways, the choice of going solar is similar to a kitchen renovation, putting an addition on the house, or building a backyard deck. Each of these investments is expensive and has benefits that are difficult to quantify, but they all have something in common: improving home value. Since homes are one of the most valuable assets many of us will ever own, these investments are not only good financial decisions but good for the long-term enjoyment we get from or homes. We can think of an investment in solar the same way we compare paying rent to paying a mortgage.

Solar PV installations, even when financed with a PPA, become a part of the customer's home, and each payment made towards the cost of the solar PV system creates some additional home value. Take our customer, Edward, for example, who has taken out a solar loan.

Although his monthly payments are going toward paying off his loan, each payment is generating more equity in his home. Had he chosen not to go solar, his monthly payments would be higher, and he would have done nothing to add value to his home.

The benefit of investing in solar can also be calculated by the re-sale value of a home. If a homeowner installs thousands of dollars' worth of solar PV equipment that saves its residents money on utility costs, it would only make sense that the home's value would rise accordingly. Studies from a number of organizations have found that homebuyers are willing to pay a premium of $15,000 for homes with an average-sized solar array already installed.[21] While the actual prices these pre-installed PV systems fetch will vary, homeowners who go solar can rest assured knowing they can not only enjoy the benefits of their investment but recoup their costs if they choose to sell their home.

In short, going solar increases home values for customers and allows them to build equity in their home—even if they go solar with a PPA. This is because buyers have a choice of whether to take over the existing PPA—benefitting from the discounted electricity rates—or the owner can simply pay off the existing PPA realize the benefits of the asset right away.

Improving home value is *the benefit a customer receives by going solar and putting their money back into their house instead of the utility company's pockets.*

---

21 U.S. Departemnt of Energy; Hoen, Ben, et.al., Environmental Energy Technologies Division; "Exploring California PV Home Premiums" December 2013 (version 2); LBNL-6484E

Financial Benefit #5: Solar Tax Credits.

The federal solar investment tax credit is perhaps the most well-known incentive and the most important for driving the solar industry's growth. However, it is not the only tax credit available, and a number of states and local municipalities have solar investment tax credits for their residents. Despite being one of the most discussed financial benefits of going solar, the federal ITC and other regional tax credits represent one of the many financial benefits of going solar.

Many homeowners going solar today are enjoying the tax returns that a solar investment provides. The tax credits are rewarded to the homeowner, business, or solar service company that pays for the installation and maintains ownership of the PV system. In other words, whoever assumes the cost of a solar PV installation—in cash or through financing—is eligible for state and federal income tax credits that are calculated from the total cost of the product. In case the investor is unable to claim the entire tax benefit in one year, the returns can be rolled over into future years.

We have already discussed the history of the federal ITC—historically, a 30 percent federal income tax credit determined by the entire cost of a solar installation—and this incentive may not last forever. The last multi-year extension approved by Congress in 2015 has the residential ITC slated to expire at the end of 2021 after decreasing to 22 percent. Although the expiration of the ITC may appear to impede at face value, some argue that it is a good thing for the long-term stability of the solar industry. A federal tax credit is certainly helpful and appreciated by investors, but the price of equipment and installations is dropping to levels that tax credits will simply not be necessary for solar to make financial sense. Furthermore, the argument that solar is only affordable because it is supported by government subsidies will be rendered impotent.

Even in the absence of a federal tax credit, there are still many state and local incentives available in competitive markets, and these mechanisms are likely to remain in up-and-coming markets. As a solar sales professional, you will be responsible for keeping up with the incentives available in your markets. There are resources available, such as the DSIRE database,[22] to help you stay up to date with incentives on a local level, understanding what financial benefits remain even after the expiration of the federal tax credit.

The solar tax credit is *the benefit customers receive in the form of an income tax return when investing in solar.*

Financial Benefit #6: Solar Production Incentives.

Some of the most successful financial tools that reward solar investments are not national or statewide tax credits calculated by the total cost of a solar PV project. Instead, they are local, utility-based incentives calculated by how much power a solar PV system produces. These *production-based incentives (PBI)* are offered by utility companies to encourage customers to install residential solar PV systems to help them meet their renewable energy portfolio goals. In addition to any tax incentives calculated by the project's total cost, a PBI is calculated by how many kWh of electricity are generated by a customer's solar PV system.

---

22 www.dsireusa.org; This is the most comprehensive source of information regarding policies and incentives in support of renewable energy and energy efficiency available in the United States.

A PBI is relatively easy to understand because utility companies already calculate electric bills by counting how many kWh a customer *consumes* and charging them a specific rate. In contrast, a PBI is calculated by counting how many kWh the customer *produces* and effectively paying them a pre-determined rate. The PBI can take many different forms, paid to the customer in a monthly check, an annual check, or simply offered as bill credits, but the overall benefit remains the same.

Similar to the federal ITC that began decreasing in 2019, many PBIs are not available perpetually and are either limited by capacity or time frame. For example, a $0.10 PBI may be available for the first 10 megawatts (MW) of solar installed, so each customer who signs up to go solar before that capacity is filled receives the benefits from that incentive. Many programs of this kind are made up of tiers, and the kWh rate will continue to step down as each tier's capacity is filled until the PBI is no longer available. This standard structure for a PBI has been employed by many utility companies in the United States. However, another version of a production incentive that has proven to be one of the most successful incentives in promoting solar power around the world is called a *feed-in tariff (FIT).*

Similar to the standard PBI discussed above, a FIT is based on how much electricity is produced by a customer's solar PV installation, but there are two distinct differences between a FIT and a traditional PBI. First, PBIs provide a financial incentive based on the *total* amount of electricity produced by a solar PV system, while a FIT is calculated by the *excess* electricity generated by the customer. Second, PBIs are generally short-term incentives that are rewarded as cash payments or bill credits that help offset the customer's utility costs. In contrast,

FITs are typically long-term agreements between the customer and their utility. The utility agrees to pay the customer a retail rate for each unit of electricity they deliver back to the grid that can then be sold to other customers on the electric grid.

Most electric utilities do not want their customers producing more power than they need, complicating the distribution grid, and taking advantage of net metering policies. PBIs reward customers with a financial incentive that supports their decision to go solar but does not encourage a customer to install more power than they need. On the other hand, FITs are more substantial incentives that essentially encourages the customer to become a net power producer and earn money by selling the power they don't use back to the utility company.

The production-based incentive is *the benefit a customer gets by earning money for each unit of electricity they produce.*

SUMMARY OF FINANCIAL BENEFITS

In most of the United States solar market, there is only one incentive available—the federal ITC—which will expire at the end of 2021 unless an extension is approved by congress. From the list of financial benefits covered in this chapter, it is hopefully becoming clear that even in the absence of the Federal ITC, there are many other financial benefits of going solar. In most cases, an investment in a residential solar PV system outweighs nearly any other home-improvement project, from kitchen renovations to home additions.

Electric bill savings and increased property values alone can allow a residential solar customer to achieve a rate of return between 8 and

10 percent—an attractive payback period when compared to other investment options. When other incentives, tax credits, and rebates are available, the rate of return from solar investments can surpass 25 percent—an almost unfathomable return for any financial investment. Calculating the financial benefits of going solar is not exactly simple, as there are many moving parts and factors to consider. However, these complicated calculations are performed by the tools and software provided by solar sales organizations to create proposals for customers.

While the financial benefits will be calculated for you, presenting these benefits to your customers is of particular importance for your success as a solar sales professional. Not only are the financial benefits the primary motivation for most customers, but approaching the subject of finance, in general, can be tricky. As you prepare to work with your customers, understanding their financial situation, calculating the return on their investment, and determining their best financial options for going solar, remember the following:

1. **Determine your customer's financial status early and without overstepping.** Find out as much as you can about your customer's financial situation so you can be prepared with the best options. In other words, don't show up with a cash proposal if the customer is unable to afford it and will be choosing between a PPA or a solar loan. Be as *informed* as you can.

2. **Never assume you know what is best for the customer.** Some customers will not share all of the details about their financial situation, so be sure not to make assumptions.

Don't assume that a customer living in a big house can afford to pay in cash or that a customer living in a smaller home does not have the financial means to pay for solar upfront. Be *prepared* for anything.

3. **Do not be afraid to offer the solution you think is best.** Only a few of the financial benefits we explored in this chapter will apply to your customers, and among them, some will apply more than others. By considering your customer's financial situation and their goals, you can determine their *best* option and focus on it throughout your presentation, avoiding the need to explain the many different possible options or financial benefits that don't apply to them. Be the *guide* to their decision.

The financial benefit of going solar is often the primary motivator for customers, but it is by no means the only reason people go solar. To truly understand our customers, we must also learn to identify the personal motivations that inspire them to invest in solar.

CHAPTER 6

THE ENVIRONMENTAL BENEFITS OF SOLAR POWER

Electricity production accounts for more than 25 percent of the total *greenhouse gas emissions* worldwide, making it the largest single contributor to climate change.[23] As a significant part of the problem, decarbonizing the electricity industry is also a major part of the solution. But reducing the environmental impact of electricity generation does not mean that we should be producing less

---

23 IPCC (2014). Climate Change 2014: Mitigation of Climate Change; Contribution of Working Group III to the Fifth Assessment Report of the Intergovernmental Panel on Climate Change; Cambridge University Press, Cambridge, United Kingdom and New York, NY, USA.

energy—in fact, humans should be using *more* electricity. So, is it possible to achieve a zero-carbon energy industry while meeting the increasing demand for electricity worldwide?

As it turns out, clean energy technology has great potential for meeting global electricity demand while preventing potential environmental damage. One of the simplest first steps toward a goal of 100 percent clean energy is producing more electricity from solar panels. However, like most development projects, there are pros and cons, so it should come as no surprise that building solar PV systems has environmental impacts.

To understand that solar energy is, in fact, a means for preventing the worst effects of climate change, we compare the environmental costs and benefits from solar power manufacturing and generation. Because most solar customers are driven more by financial savings than avoided greenhouse gas emissions, the purpose of this chapter is not to prove how good solar is for the environment but to explore the features of solar that make it a cleaner and more sustainable alternative to fossil fuels.

THE ENVIRONMENTAL BENEFITS OF SOLAR

A few hundred square miles of solar panels tucked away in the Mojave Desert could theoretically supply the United States with all the electricity it needs. However, there are reasons this will never happen: for one, a centralized power plant of this size would require vast, expensive transmission lines to carry the electricity all across the country. Another reason is because of land-use concerns and impacts on natural ecosystems created by large construction projects.

Simply put, installing large-scale power generation facilities like solar panels or wind farms can have similar *upfront* environmental and social impacts to their fossil fuel counterparts. These large-scale solar installations are referred to as *utility-scale solar* projects because they are typically built for power companies to sell electricity to their customers.

Large solar arrays can be safely placed where fossil fuel power plants cannot, but they are still land-intensive construction projects that may disrupt ecosystems and surrounding communities. Forests, grasslands, and even deserts play an important role in absorbing carbon dioxide, so cutting down trees or disrupting land to build a solar generation facility releases large quantities of carbon dioxide. When planned properly, large-scale solar projects can be preferable because of lower development costs, but there is another way to install solar that completely avoids land-use concerns: *rooftop solar*.

Installing distributed rooftop solar has the same environmental benefit as large, land-intensive solar projects and avoids the negative externalities caused by centralized generation facilities. The growth of distributed energy resources like rooftop solar is effectively reducing the environmental impacts of electricity generation as a whole. Land preservation is one direct benefit of increasing distributed solar resources, but there are indirect benefits as well. The utility industry saves billions of dollars normally spent fixing outdated and broken-down sections of the electric grid. Avoided maintenance and upgrade work means fewer utility trucks are dispatched, further preventing emissions from gas-powered utility vehicles.

Utilizing millions of square miles of otherwise unused roof space around the world significantly lowers the chance of causing social or environmental harm compared to traditional generation methods and even other forms of renewable energy. However, even rooftop solar does not completely avoid the possibility of environmental impacts. Throughout the lifetime of a solar panel, from manufacturing to installation to removal and recycling, there are associated greenhouse gas emissions and the potential for pollution from hazardous materials.

In the remainder of this chapter, we will take all of the impacts from solar into consideration, which are collectively referred to as the *lifecycle impacts* of solar. By exploring these impacts and comparing them to fossil fuels, we prepare ourselves for explaining the environmental benefits to customers in a way that makes sense and provides peace of mind that solar is, in fact, a cleaner and healthier alternative to traditional power generation.

ENVIRONMENTAL IMPACTS VS. BENEFITS

Environmental Impact #1: Greenhouse Gas Emissions.

During the lifecycle of a solar power plant, the greenhouse gas emissions are not zero. However, most of the environmental impacts from solar are associated with the heavy-duty machinery and vehicles used for mining the raw materials that go into solar panels. Manufacturing facilities use large amounts of energy, which does not always come from clean and renewable sources. Once the solar panels have been completed, they must be delivered to customers by gas-powered trucks. These impacts and emissions that result from manufacturing solar panels are currently unavoidable with modern infrastructure. However, once solar panels are installed, they will produce electricity for decades without creating any more harmful emissions.

When we compare the emissions from solar power to fossil fuels, we see some very obvious differences. The most evident is that fossil fuel power generation requires combustion—burning fuels like coal and natural gas—which releases tremendous amounts of greenhouse gases. Once a fossil fuel power plant begins operating, it will produce emissions over its entire lifetime or as long as it continues burning fuel. The emissions that fossil fuel power plants create are in addition to those related to the mining, transportation, and refining process, but fossil fuels do not need to be burned to cause harm. Natural gas is largely made up of methane, which is more than 25 times more harmful than carbon dioxide,[24] and it doesn't need to be burned to cause the heat-trapping effect known to contribute to global warming and climate change.

Environmental Benefit #1: Greenhouse gas emissions are lower and upfront.

Despite the emissions created by manufacturing solar panels, they're overall significantly less than those from fossil fuels and occur on a much shorter timeline. Almost all of the emissions associated with solar energy production occur before the solar panels are even installed and begin producing electricity. Only when solar panels are decommissioned and recycled will there be any additional emissions.

The following table illustrates the difference between emissions of solar power and compares the *lifecycle emissions* of solar to other sources of electricity to generate one kWh of electricity:

---

24 U.S. Environmental Protection Agency (EPA); Greenhouse Gas Emissions: Understanding Global Warming Potentials; https://www.epa.gov/ghgemissions/understanding-global-warming-potentials (Accessed August 2020)

Energy Source	Lifetime Emissions per kWh
Solar PV	14 - 41 g CO_2e *
Wind	11 g CO_2e
Nuclear	12 g CO_2e
Coal (with Carbon Capture & Storage)	220 g CO_2e
Natural Gas (with Carbon Capture & Storage)	170 g CO_2e
Hydropower	24 g CO_2e
BioFuel	240 g CO_2e

Fig.11 Lifetime Emissions per kWh[25]

To put this in a larger context, the United Nations climate goals for maintaining a global average warming under two degrees Celsius requires a significant decrease in emissions by 2050—only nuclear and renewable energy sources will achieve this goal.

Although the manufacturing and installation process results in greenhouse gas emissions, these impacts are offset after just two years of generating electricity from solar panels.[26] In other words,

---

25 IPCC Working Group III – Mitigation of Climate Change, Annex III: Technology – specific cost and performance parameters – Table A.III.2 (Emissions of selected electricity supply technologies (gCO2eq/kWh). IPCC. 2014.

26 National Renewable Energy Laboratory (NREL); U.S. Deparmetn of Energy Office of Energy Efficiency and Renewable Energy; DOE/GO-102004-1847 January 2004; https://www.nrel.gov/docs/fy13osti/56487.pdf (accessed October 2020)

---

* The range of Lifetime Emissions per kWh for solar photovoltaics differs for rooftop solar at the low end of the spectrum and utility-scale solar projects that have more associated emissions.

the benefits of solar—the avoided greenhouse gas emissions from replacing other energy sources—significantly outweigh the impacts. When selling solar to customers concerned about its environmental impacts, *help them understand the difference in lifecycle emissions from solar compared to other sources of electricity.*

Environmental Impact #2: Harmful Chemical Pollutants.

The predominant material used in solar cells is silicon, which is derived from quartz, the most abundant mineral compound found at Earth's surface. Mining quartz and turning it into the silicon needed for solar panels results in greenhouse gas emissions, but there are also some harmful chemicals required to manufacture solar cells. One of these harmful chemicals is silicon tetrachloride, which can burn human skin, cause respiratory illnesses, and form hydrochloric acid when exposed to water. This chemical and a handful of other compounds used by panel manufacturers are contained and recycled in the manufacturing process to make new silicon solar cells. Nevertheless, the potential harm to human and environmental health is lessened if proper safety measures and control of these chemicals is successful.

If we consider the harmful chemicals used to manufacture solar cells as necessary for power production, then it would make sense to compare other sources of power. In the following graph, the number of harmful chemicals needed to make a solar cell is compared to those used in the fracking of natural gas:

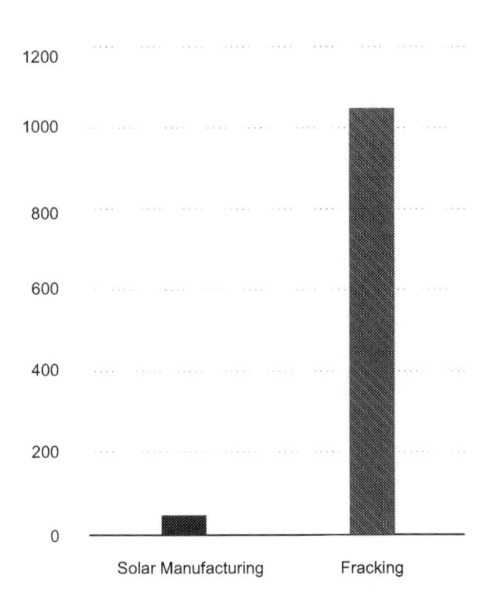

Fig 12. Known Harmful Chemicals[27]

When we compare solar power to natural gas, we clearly see that the *eight* harmful chemicals necessary for manufacturing solar cells are dwarfed by over a thousand compounds used in the daily operations of the fossil fuel industry. There are countless chemicals in hydraulic fracturing fluid—many of which are undisclosed—that are injected directly into the earth's crust every day.

Environmental Benefit #2: Avoiding Pollution and Chemical Spills.

The number of hazardous chemicals used to manufacture solar panels is significantly lower than what is required by the fossil fuel industry. In addition to using *fewer* chemicals, solar panels are made in controlled facilities where hazardous compounds left over from

27 Elliott, E., Ettinger, A., Leaderer, B. et al. A systematic evaluation of chemicals in hydraulic-fracturing fluids and wastewater for reproductive and developmental toxicity. J Expo Sci Environ Epidemiol 27, 90–99 (2017). https://doi.org/10.1038/ jes.2015.81

the manufacturing process can be recycled and used to make new silicon cells. As the industry grows and technology improves, the risk of harmful materials from solar manufacturing polluting the natural environment is decreasing even further. Meanwhile, fossil fuels are becoming more complicated to extract. Infrastructure is failing more frequently, causing oil spills and pipeline leaks that damage entire ecosystems, poison water resources, and endanger the health of humans and wildlife alike—not to mention the harm to regional economies that depend on healthy natural resources.

As with any modern technology, the use of harmful chemicals is a necessary part of the manufacturing process. While there is a marginal level of risk in the manufacturing of solar panels, the overall risk of toxic chemicals harming human health or damaging natural ecosystems is significantly lower compared to traditional fossil fuel sources. When selling solar to customers who are concerned about harmful chemical pollution, *help them understand that the amount of toxic chemicals needed for solar panel manufacturing is significantly lower than other sources of power.*

Environmental Impact #3: Land Use.

In the solar industry, land use is primarily a concern for large-scale solar projects that disturb natural ecosystems, leading to carbon dioxide emissions and drastically altering natural landscapes. As with any large-scale construction project, the land where solar projects are developed becomes effectively unusable for any other purposes, and in some cases, developers will trim or remove trees and other vegetation because solar requires uninterrupted access to sunlight.

Fossil fuel power plants cause the same problems, and there are two reasons traditional generation facilities are built far away from population centers: they produce many harmful emissions and pollutants, and they require a relatively large amount of space. Fossil fuel power plants take up millions of acres of land in the United States because of their large footprint, but also because the surrounding land becomes degraded and dangerously polluted. In addition, strip mines and mountain-top removal operations that are common for fossil fuel extraction cause irreversible damage to large swaths of land and alter natural landscapes for millions of years.

Environmental Benefit #3: Land Preservation.

While large-scale solar projects produce more greenhouse emissions and take up acres of land area, rooftop solar avoids both of these concerns entirely. Not only does rooftop solar cost less than ground-mounted solar projects—from both a financial and environmental perspective—they make use of otherwise unused surface area for the production of electricity. When selling solar to customers concerned about the conservation of land, *help them understand that rooftop solar prevents the unnecessary development of virgin lands.*

Impact of Solar #4: Human Health Risks.

To understand the potential health impacts of solar power development, we must consider the short-term and long-term risks as well as the overall impact that solar has on human health. In the short-term, there are inherent physical risks in the mining, transportation, and manufacturing processes. There is also an additional physical risk during the installation process that requires workers to climb on rooftops. However, the long-term risks of solar are virtually non-existent—aside from the potential of acute exposure to the toxic chemicals used to make solar cells—because once solar panels are installed, they pose no further risks.

The dangers of mining and manufacturing are not unique to the solar industry. The same risks exist in fossil fuel mining and development operations, but coal mining and fracking operations are also directly related to respiratory illnesses such as black lung and increased cancer rates from continued exposure to an unknown number of harmful chemicals. Perhaps more disturbing is the fact that human health risks from fossil fuels are not limited to employees. The following graph illustrates how this compares to the deaths caused by air pollution and accidents from other sources of power:

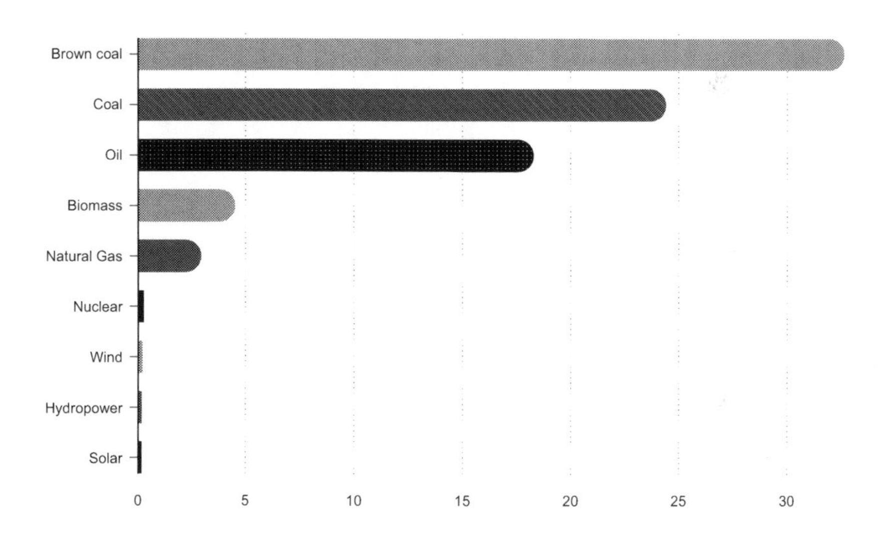

Fig 13. Death Rates from Energy Production[28]

---

28 Our World in Data, "Death rates from energy production per terawatt-hour (TWh)"; OurWorldInData.org/energy; https://ourworldindata.org/grapher/deathrates-from-energy-production-per-twh (Accessed October 2020); This data combines two sources: Markandya, A., & Wilkinson, P. (2007) assessed the death rates from accidents and air pollution major energy sources (fossil fuels, nuclear and biomass). Sovacool et al. (2016) assessed death rates from accidents from low-carbon energy sources (nuclear and renewables) based on historical records spanning the period 1990 to 2013.

Over three and a half million deaths can be attributed to outdoor pollution caused by fossil fuels each year. Communities located near fracking sites, coal mines, or fossil fuel refineries have higher rates of cancer, lung disease, and many other developmental health problems. To make matters worse, fossil fuel facilities are typically situated nearer to low-income communities who will not only bear the worst of these health effects but feel the worst effects of climate change, which will only create more health problems.

Environmental Benefit #4: Protecting human health.

There are few more important reasons to replace fossil fuels with clean, renewable energy sources than human health. Fossil fuels are responsible for more deaths due to air pollution, accidents, and toxic emissions than any other source of electricity. Replacing fossil fuel power generation with solar protects human healthy by limiting the short-term accidental deaths from fossil fuel development, preventing long-term health effects of air pollution, and decreasing the overall impacts on human health in the energy sector. When selling solar to customers concerned about their health and the environment, *help them understand how solar reduces human health risks posed by the power sector.*

Impact of Solar #5: Water Use and Pollution.

Most manufacturing processes consume water, and this is true in the process of making solar panels. If safety protocols are ineffective, toxic chemicals needed in manufacturing can pollute the environment and end up in water resources. Freshwater resources are essential for human health, environmental health, and economic stability, among many other reasons. However, these resources are heavily impacted by the existing energy industry.

Compared to the fossil fuel industry, renewable energy sources use practically no water. In fact, the fossil fuel industry in the United States is responsible for 41 percent of the country's freshwater needs each year.

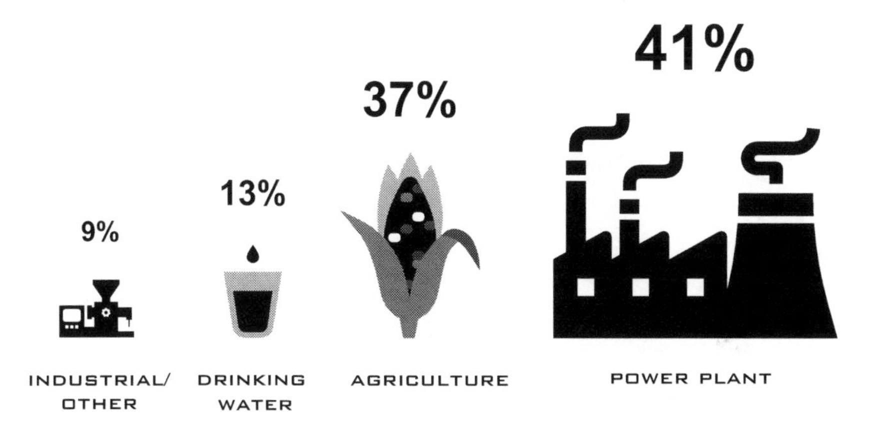

Fig. 14 Fresh Water Needs[29]

Fossil fuel operations consume trillions of gallons of fresh water each year, primarily for cooling power plants, but also in the extraction, refining, and transportation of fossil fuels. Oil spills are the most well-known cause of water pollution from the fossil fuel industry, but fracking and coal mining are less visible causes of water pollution that damages ecosystems and contaminates drinking water.

Environmental Benefit #5: Protecting Water Resources.

Compared to the manufacturing of solar panels in controlled facilities, fossil fuel operations take place wherever resources are found, which has a much greater chance of directly polluting natural

29 Union of Concerned Scientists (UCS); "Power and Water At Risk: The Energy-Water Collision" Published Jun 2, 2011, Updated September 2012; https://www.ucsusa.org/resources/power-and-water-risk (Accessed October 2020)

resources and waterways. When selling solar to customers who are concerned about the environment, *help them understand that solar power uses practically no water and helps minimize water use and pollution from fossil fuels.*

SUMMARY OF ENVIRONMENTAL BENEFITS

There are many other impacts and benefits to consider when comparing solar to other forms of electricity generation. In the end, we must accept that almost everything we do has some environmental impact because fossil fuels largely drive our modern world. Until electric automobiles replace gas-guzzling utility vehicles and renewable energy sources power the heavy machinery we depend on, it will be virtually impossible to eliminate greenhouse gas emissions in the power sector—even if the energy supply were 100 percent renewable energy. However, we must acknowledge that while solar power may not completely eliminate the emissions or environmental impacts, it does significantly lower the risks compared to fossil fuels and most other energy sources.

Shifting to a renewable-based energy industry will require an increasing amount of renewable energy generation and improved energy storage technologies, and a mix of clean energy tools that include carbon capture and storage (CCS) and other zero-carbon fuels. In addition, a clean energy future will depend on upgraded transmission infrastructure and energy management software systems that help manage new, intermittent energy technologies such as solar while continuing to meet the growing demand for electricity.

Solar power is becoming more popular than ever. A clean energy economy can meet the global demand for energy *and* protect our planet from the worst effects of climate change. While most residential solar customers are comforted by the environmental benefits of going solar, few are choosing to install solar panels entirely for these reasons. Nevertheless, learning to explain the environmental benefits of solar to customers who are unsure whether it is the right thing to do will help you bring your customers to the right decision for the planet: the decision to go solar.

CHAPTER 7

THE FEATURES OF SOLAR POWER

So far, we've learned about the financial benefits that solar customers receive from solar and the key motivators that lead them to decide to go solar. In the previous chapters, we explored the environmental benefits of solar that also play a role in the decision-making process. When a customer chooses to go solar, they can rest assured knowing they are earning an attractive rate of return and protecting the planet, but what does the customer experience once they have installed solar?

These experiences are the features that a customer enjoys when they go solar and will continue to enjoy throughout the lifetime of their solar project. We can refer to these experiences either as the *ser-*

vice-based benefits or the *features of solar* that play an important role over the lifetime of a solar project.

Some of the following service-based benefits are experienced by all homeowners who go solar. Others are specific to a PPA or cash purchase, while others are regionally specific. As we know, the process of selling is highly emotional, so understanding what features and benefits are most important to your customer will guide you toward the best solution *for them*. Understanding these features is not a matter of memorizing them or deciding which is more important than the other. Instead, your goal will be to learn how to determine which are most valuable and important to your customer.

TURNKEY INSTALLATION

Most solar companies today take care of everything for their customers. This means that once a customer enters into a solar contract, they have virtually nothing to do but sit back and wait for their fully operational solar PV system to be installed, which we call a *turnkey installation*.

The term "turnkey" refers to much more than an operational solar installation, and most customers are unaware of the many steps that must be taken in the process of completing a residential solar project. From utility interconnection applications to procuring the solar panels and materials for installation to processing and applying for any available incentives and tax credits, turnkey solar installers take care of it all.

As a solar sales professional, your job is to present solar installations with all these steps taken care of on behalf of the customer. This also means that you can avoid wasting your time with prospective customers who aren't interested in a turnkey installation or who want to install solar panels themselves. To serve your customers better, *focus your time and energy on selling the ease of a turnkey installation that takes care of the entire process for customers.*

CUSTOMIZED SOLUTIONS

One of the reasons going solar makes financial sense is because solar can be customized to provide only as much power as a customer needs—or desires. There are many variables and external factors that can dictate how many solar panels a homeowner can install on their property, and for this reason, going solar is a highly customizable process.

Solar PV systems are designed specifically for each customer for three primary reasons: first, every house is a different size and shape, so solar panels must be designed specifically for the roof on which they are installed. Second, even if two houses have the same roof design, their inhabitants will likely have different usage habits and consumption, so the system size will depend on how much power they use. Finally, solar PV systems are designed to meet the customer's financial goals and personal preferences.

Some companies offer "solar kits" to customers but selling pre-designed PV systems is often better for the company than for the customer. Solar companies can reduce operating costs by selling the same system over and over and streamlining their installations. However, in most cases, your customers will do better in the long run if they customize a right-sized system that uses the right equipment than from saving a few hundred dollars on the total cost of their project.

Focusing on customization and design decisions that customers have control over enables the customer to enjoy the process of going solar even more. To serve your customers better, *focus on maximizing their buy-in and their financial benefits by customization and right-sizing their PV system.*

PV SYSTEM MONITORING

Keeping track of power production is important for ensuring that a PV system is operating as expected, although system monitoring has not always been automatically available to customers. Historically, monitoring has been an add-on that customers have to pay for because it requires additional hardware, an internet connection to share production data, and access to online portal software. However, this important feature is becoming more common and can also be achieved without paying extra.

Solar production monitoring occurs in the inverter—where all the electricity generated from panels will flow to be converted into AC power—so the type of equipment installed will determine how the customer can access their production data. String inverters, or central inverters, are installed inside the customer's home and have built-in displays that show current and lifetime power production. Micro-inverters are attached to the solar panels, so monitoring is only possible with monitoring software or additional hardware. If monitoring is a priority for customers, then choosing the right equipment is important, but inverters are not the only way to monitor production.

Monitoring is an important feature that gives customers the tools to ensure their system is functioning properly, but monthly solar production data is provided to grid-connected customers on their electric bills each month. To serve your customers better, *determine how important PV System Monitoring is to them and selecting the best equipment to meet their goals.*

PRODUCTION GUARANTEES

Explaining how much power your customer's solar panels will generate over the next twenty years can be a challenge—and *telling* a customer how much power they will produce is a far cry from *assuring* them. A *production guarantee* provides solar customers with the peace of mind that their solar PV system will live up to their expectations and that they will not be held responsible if it doesn't. However, production guarantees are not a standard offering in the solar industry, and this feature is typically only available to customers who go solar through a PPA.

The reason for this is not because solar production estimates are unsupported. In fact, most production estimates come from the publicly accessible data from the National Renewable Energy Laboratory's *PVWatts* tool.[30] In the absence of production guarantees, this tool offers an effective way to show your customer how production data is calculated. It also compares your conservative estimates to your competitors who inflate their production estimates.

---

30 www.pvwatts.nrel.gov – The National Renewable Energy Laboratory is operated by the U.S. Department of Energy. This tool serves as the solar industry standard for estimating production of grid-connected PV energy systems.

Production guarantees are available for PPA customers because solar service companies charge their customers for the power they *produce*, so any interruption in power generation is a problem that the company will be motivated to fix as soon as possible. Most PPA contracts include terms describing what happens if the system doesn't produce as much power as the customer is paying for. To serve your customers better, *help them understand how power production is guaranteed or by supporting your production estimates with evidence when production guarantees are not possible.*

WARRANTIES

When guaranteeing a solar PV system's performance is not possible, the assurances that warranties provide are extremely helpful in providing peace of mind to customers. There are two categories of warranties: *workmanship warranties, which* are important to customers when choosing which solar installer to work with, and *equipment warranties,* which help decide what equipment to install on their homes.

Workmanship warranties are typically between five and ten years and cover all aspects of the construction and installation of solar equipment on a customer's home. Five-year workmanship warranties are fairly standard, but these warranties are only as good as the companies that stand behind them. Workmanship warranties are not only important for customers but also for the sales professionals who want to feel confident that their company prioritizes high-quality work and, therefore, will be more likely to stay in business and continue serving their customers. There is always the risk of a solar company going out of business, even as the solar industry as a whole continues to thrive, which is why equipment warranties help customers feel more secure with their investment.

Equipment warranties apply specifically to the solar panels and inverters that ensure a PV system will continue to produce electricity for decades to come.* These are not only the most expensive parts of a solar PV system, but also the most critical for power production. These components are often protected by two separate warranties. First, the *production warranties* guarantee that solar panels will generate electricity at a certain efficiency over the panel's lifetime. Second, the *material warranties* ensure the solar panel will hold up from exposure to the elements over time. Material warranties also protect from any manufacturing defects and other kinds of damages unrelated to energy production.

One of the most appealing features for homeowners who go solar is knowing that if there are any issues with their installation or problems with their equipment, they will be covered by warranties for up to twenty-five years. To serve your customers better, *work for a company that does high-quality work and will stand behind their workmanship warranties.*

Furthermore, to serve your customers better, *help them choose the best equipment for their project that lives up to their expectations of performance and warranty coverage.*

---

*Racking and other hardware required for the installation of solar panels and inverters have their own warranties. These materials ar e typically made from aluminum or alloy metals designed to withstand exposur e to the elements over extended periods of time, and with no moving parts they have ve ry low chances of failure over the lifetime of a solar installation.

CUSTOMER SERVICE

At the core of the service-based benefits that homeowners enjoy from going solar is the *customer service* that begins with the sales cycle and lasts long after the contract is signed. As a solar sales professional, you will have total control of your customers throughout the sales cycle, but once the contract is signed, the customer's experience truly begins.

Solar panels and the components of PV systems are designed to withstand direct sunlight and exposure to the elements for decades. If there are any problems with the installation or equipment, that is what the warranties are for. So, customers who worry about service or maintenance really just want to know that from the moment they sign the contract to go solar, they will be taken care of. The truth is that solar PV systems have no moving parts, and when equipment is installed properly, it will function for over thirty years without much additional attention or maintenance needed. For this reason, ensuring good customer service during the first stages of going solar can have a long-standing impact on their experience with solar in general.

Customer service is defined by a few factors, and it is important to familiarize yourself with how your company interacts with customers and deals with issues. Once a contract is signed, other team members and departments will begin contacting the customer and arriving at their home for site audits, installations, and inspections. To prepare your customer for this experience, you must be familiar with each step in the process and remain their primary point of contact as long as possible.

Larger companies often have entire departments dedicated to customer care and handling accounts, but automated phone systems can be frustrating and impersonal for customers when each time they call, they speak with somebody different. In a smaller company, customers are more likely to reach somebody directly if they call with questions or concerns. However, fewer employees means they have less bandwidth to address issues right away. In either case, the relationship you create with your customers is just as important as trusting that your company and colleagues will live up to their service expectations. The less time you spend dealing with customer concerns or disappointment, the more time you can spend finding new customers.

The service benefits of solar are mostly intangible to the customer, but they're important for creating happy customers—that leads to positive company reviews and referrals. To serve your customers better, *help them understand how your company handles customer service, ensuring you will be there to help with anything they might need.*

LONG-TERM VALUE

The process of going solar is exciting for customers, but most of the action occurs during the first few months when they get to decide on system designs, watch their panels get installed, and finally begin to produce their own electricity. In the months that follow, rebates and tax credits provide even more short-term satisfaction and joy. However, the value of solar continues long after panels are installed.

The financial benefits of solar persist for many years, and in most cases, they only continue to increase over time. The higher the electric utility bills go, the more money your customers will save, so the long-term value can actually be much greater than what is anticipated and presented to customers upfront. However, the long-term value of solar is not just the financial benefit but also the experience of energy security, peace-of-mind, community improvement, environmental protection, and even more opportunities to take advantage of new technology.

One long-term value that is often overlooked is the potential for making choices in the future that would not be possible without solar. This is becoming clear as battery back-up systems are now more affordable and growing in popularity. Homeowners with solar are better positioned to add battery storage to their home and further increase their energy security.

Solar power also protects your customers' homes. In areas that are prone to hail damage, solar panels are more durable than some kinds of roofing materials and can actually protect your customer's roof from weather damage. This means long-term protection of the home, which is not included in the calculation of financial benefits when going solar.

Finally, the community value of solar is often overlooked. Not only does solar add value to your customers' homes, but higher home values in residential areas also raises the value of the neighborhood and may even be an indication of healthier, happier, and more valuable areas. Going solar doesn't only enrich those who install the solar panels. It brings value to the local economy as a whole. To serve your customers better, *help them understand the long-term value and opportunities that going solar provides.*

SUPPORTING LOCAL ECONOMIES

The rapid growth of the solar industry has created a significant amount of opportunity in communities all around the world. Local "mom and pop shops" and national solar companies create thousands of jobs for engineers, electricians, installers, accountants, and countless others. Solar panel manufacturers employ scientists, skilled workers, product managers, and many other team members. All of the economic activity in the solar industry stimulates political attention and supports utility-driven campaigns to increase solar capacity. Each homeowner who chooses to go solar is contributing to the growth of the solar industry and is directly supporting their local economy.

If you work for a small company that only installs solar in your area, it can be easy to relate these benefits to your customers and show how your work supports the local economy. Your customers are the reason you have your job, and they are an essential part of the solar industry. However, even customers who choose to go solar with national corporations are contributing to their local communities.

Solar companies employ people at their headquarters, which might be located across the country, but they also create jobs in the communities they work in. This can give your customers—and you as well—the positive feeling of supporting the local economy. When your customer goes solar, they're not just saving money for themselves. They're also creating economic opportunities and jobs for many others. Going solar creates jobs on a local scale for the installers, engineers, and project managers who install PV systems. To serve your customers better, *help them understand that by choosing to go solar, they are also supporting their local economy, even if their solar company's headquarters are out of town.*

SELLING WITH INTEGRITY

Most of the benefits we've discussed in this chapter are difficult to quantify, but they can play an important role in defining the overall experience a customer has when they go solar. In addition to the features we've covered so far, there is one that every single one of your customers can directly benefit from: their experience working with *you*.

One of the most important features for customers looking into solar is the opportunity to work with a sales professional who treats them with respect and integrity, presents their options with honesty and accuracy, and most importantly, approaches sales as something they do *for* them and not *to* them.

Throughout your sales career, you will lose sales to competitors, and some of your prospects will simply not go solar. Failing to close a sale is no reason to despair, but it is instead an opportunity to reflect, improve, and learn how to be more prepared for your next customer.

Some prospects will decide not to go solar because they can't produce as much power as they want. A dishonest response would be inflating production estimates to convince them they can produce more electricity. Some prospects will not go solar because a ten-year payback is too long. A dishonest response would be inflating the growth rate of utility prices to show a better payback. While these may seem minor, they are deceptions that both you and your customer will have to live with for decades.

Each opportunity you have to sell solar to a customer is a chance to help customers understand exactly what features and benefits they can expect to enjoy from solar—and to do it with integrity. To serve your customers better, *help them understand exactly what financial returns, service benefits, and features of solar they can expect over the lifetime of their solar PV system.*

SUMMARY OF THE FEATURES OF SOLAR POWER

Of all the features or service-based benefits we have discussed in this chapter, each one could be enough to earn the business of your future customers. Similarly, the absence of one may deter a customer from going solar. Some of your customers will care more about customer service, while others are adamant about supporting local businesses. To become a top solar sales professional, you must learn how and when each of these features and benefits appeal to customers.

The first step to selling solar effectively to customers is learning how to relate the benefits of solar directly to them. While these benefits will remain largely the same for years to come, all of your customers will have different goals and values. As you approach the customer, your first goal will be getting to know them and learning what is most important to them. Once you know who you are selling to and what features and benefits to focus on, you can relate the benefits of solar directly to their situation, their values, and their goals. This might sound easy and straightforward, but it takes practice, experience, and most importantly—a solid sales method.

In the first two parts of this book, we have built a solid foundation of knowledge about how solar works and why customers choose to go solar. In Part 3, we will learn the *Solar Sales Method,* which will help you sell solar more effectively and with more success.

The following chapters won't teach you more about how solar works or explain how to manipulate customers into signing up to go solar, but instead, they will teach you how to tell the story of going solar. Your customers don't just want to learn about solar panels and be enticed by too-good-to-be-true offers. They want to believe in the choice they are making. This becomes possible when your customer can imagine their future with more money in the bank, improved energy security, and a cleaner, healthier environment.

The story you will learn to tell your customers is not about you and your knowledge of solar—nor is it just about how much money solar saves. The story you will learn to tell is about your customers, and the more they believe in the story you are telling, the more they will see that they have control over their story. When you are successful, your customers will choose to go down this path with you. In addition, they're more likely to tell their story to others who will want to find out what is possible for them.

Where does this story begin? With the characters. Your customers are the characters at the center of each story you will tell throughout your career. When the customer is at the center of the sales process, there is no room for manipulation or deceit because they know their story. Honesty and integrity are more powerful stories that your customers will *feel* better about. Until you understand your customers and they are willing to listen to your story, the selling cannot truly begin.

As you learn the solar sales method in the chapters ahead, try not to imagine yourself at the end of the process—asking the customer to sign a contract. Instead of putting pressure on *closing the sale*, remember that signing a contract takes a few seconds, while the sales process can last for weeks, even months, and solar panels will last for decades. If you learn to enjoy the process and practice focusing on building relationships, discovering problems, and presenting solutions, your success will come more easily. If you do these things well, closing the sale will come naturally, easily, and you will spend more of your time enjoying the process of helping your customers rather than trying to get their signatures.

PART 3

SELLING SOLAR: THE "SOLAR SALES METHOD"

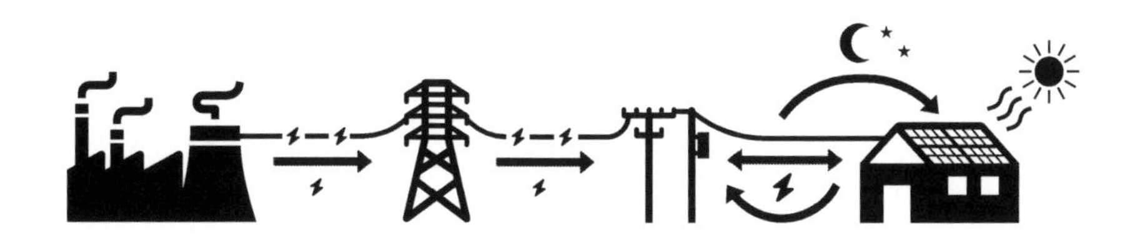

CHAPTER 8

STEP 1 - THE INTERVIEW: DISCOVER

Now that you know how solar works and the many reasons why homeowners choose to go solar, it's time to learn how to apply this knowledge to selling solar more effectively using the *Solar Sales Method*. Before we dive into the method, it's worth acknowledging one more time that *selling is more emotional than logical*. In other words, understanding your customers and establishing a relationship built on trust and open communication is just as important as learning about solar technology and policy. So, what's the first step to high-performance solar sales?

You may have already guessed it: understanding the customer that you are selling to. This means focusing on what is most important to *them*, getting to know them personally, finding out their preferences, and learning about their lifestyle and energy habits so you can present them with the best solution to meet their needs. All of this happens during *the interview,* the first step of the Solar Sales Method.

The primary goal of the interview is to *discover* the customer—a process that is often referred to as "building rapport" in sales culture—and it is a critical first step to effective communication and finding out their needs. The purpose of the interview is to develop a relationship—an emotional connection—with the customer to facilitate a more open and understanding sales process. There are three ground rules for an effective interview:

Interview Rule #1: Listen. Listen. Listen.

Learning about the customer is not possible when you're talking, so the more you wish to learn, the better you must become at listening. Practicing how to listen intently is as important as learning to approach customers in a way that will cause them to feel comfortable opening up to you. This ability may take practice and experience, but it is made possible by showing interest in getting to know your customer and welcoming their responses to your questions. The interview is not the time to trade stories but to hear about your customer—for instance, not asking about them and then talking about yourself, which is likely to show that you're not *actually* interested in them. The first rule to the interview is to provide your customer with the space to talk about themselves and to listen intently.

Interview Rule #2: Do Not Start Selling.

Most sales professionals at the top of their field understand that before you can start selling, you have to know who you're selling to. This is especially true in the solar industry, where a relatively large amount of information is required to come up with an accurate design and price for a solar installation. Diving straight into a sales pitch not only limits your knowledge of the customer but misses the opportunity to make sure the customer understands that *you* are more than some person trying to sell something *to* them. The interview is not the time to start promoting the benefits of solar or talking about the expertise of you and your company. The second ground rule of the interview to focus on getting to know who you're selling to *before* the selling begins.

Rule #3: Take Notes.

No matter how long you work in sales, you'll never remember everything your customers say to you. Taking notes throughout the interview—and the entire sales process—is not just about writing down answers to the questions you ask. You must also keep track of details that will help you later on in the sales process, including figures and data about the customer's lifestyle and energy consumption as well as subtle cues about their interests, goals, and opinions about solar energy and what they expect from it. Taking notes has the added benefit of avoiding asking the same question twice, which can be frustrating to your customers—*"I already told you this. Aren't you listening?"*

Start the interview with a blank piece of paper in your notebook or a *customer account worksheet* (an example is provided in the Appendix) to begin keeping track of the details you learn about your customer. The third ground rule of the interview is to keep an organized log of notes detailing the information you learn about your customer.

HOW TO INTERVIEW YOUR CUSTOMERS

Although the first step of the Solar Sales Method is called an "interview," it does not mean that you should grill your customer with questions about their life or dig up personal information about them. The action word for the interview is *discover*, which means it is the time to find out as much relevant information as you can about your customers with two goals in mind. The first goal is to show that you are genuinely interested in getting to know them—and not just focused on selling your product. The second goal is to ensure that you have all the specific information you need to develop a compelling solar proposal customized for their needs.

The interview doesn't just begin when you show up to a sales meeting. It starts when you have your first conversation with the customer, whether that is over the phone, via email, or in person. However, the interview will always be the first step in the sales process—before any selling begins. Developing effective interview skills takes practice, and it may take some time to resist the urge to start selling right away, but there is no substitute for experience.

Learning about your customer requires two types of questions that become natural with practice, both of which are essential to truly discovering your customers. These are *on-topic questions* related to solar and *off-topic questions* related to the customer and their personal situation.

On-Topic Questions: At the beginning of the sales process, it is natural to ask your customers about solar. These questions are an important part of the qualification process—making sure your customer is a good candidate for solar. They also help determine the details you need to design a solar PV system to meet the customer's needs. Examples of on-topic questions are:

- ***"What made you decide to look into solar?"***
- ***"How long have you been considering going solar?"***
- ***"How much electricity do you use?"***
- ***"What do you hope to achieve by going solar?"***
- ***"Do you have any concerns about going solar?"***
- ***"Have you ever gotten a solar quote before?"***

These kinds of questions are important during the interview, but it's worth noting that the lead generation process tends to focus on these kinds of questions, so your customers may have already answered them before.

Asking questions related to solar will result in answers related to solar. By listening closely to their answers, you can begin to understand your customer more clearly—their personality, opinions, concerns, and preconceptions. You will also learn what they *know* about solar and what they *think* about solar. The most important goal of the interview is learning what the customer *needs* from solar. The best way to develop an emotional understanding of customers is simply by asking.

Off-Topic Questions: Selling solar *for* your customer begins with discovering who they are, what is most important to them, and identifying a problem they have that only solar will solve. Selling solar *to* homeowners by explaining all of the benefits is a much different approach than understanding what challenges your customer is experiencing and what goals they have before presenting solar as a solution and a means of achieving their goals.

To appeal to your customers' emotional needs during the sales process, you also need to ask questions to get them to talk about themselves. Some examples of these off-topic questions are:

- ***"How long have you lived in this your home?"***
- ***"Did you grow up around here?"***
- ***"What kind of work do you do?"***
- ***"How did you get into your profession?"***
- ***"What do you do in your free time?"***
- ***"How do you balance your busy schedule with your family?"***

There is a fine line between asking too many personal questions or asking questions that are *too personal*. In some cases, the examples above may be inappropriate or irrelevant for your customers. However, the more you practice having these conversations with customers, the better you will become at recognizing which questions will produce an informative answer, how many to ask, and when to ask them.

There are a number of different personality types, so you shouldn't expect to approach each of your customers with the same questions. You can usually get a sense of their personality during the first conversation. Are they talkative and open about their personal life? Or more restrained and harder to get talking? Having a handle on who they are will help you prepare for the interview. It's difficult to ask questions, listen intently, take notes, and try to deduce your customer's personality type at the same time. For this reason, learn as much as you can before the interview to arrive prepared with questions tailored specifically for the customer.

Whenever possible, a portion of the interview should take place before the sales appointment, either over the phone or in person. A "pre-qualification" phone call before the sales appointment not only allows more time to prepare for the rest of the sales process, it can also shorten the interview during your sales meeting and save both you and your customer a lot of time.

The primary purpose of the interview is to discover who you will be presenting solar to so you can approach them with the best possible solution. Your primary goal is to find out what your customer needs to hear to *want* to go solar. The challenge in this step is identifying a problem that your customer has with their current situation that can be solved by solar.

DISCOVERING THE PROBLEM

There are many reasons why homeowners choose to go solar, but almost all of them ultimately make the decision because it solves a "problem" that they have. Homeowners who are fully aware that they have a problem will make statements like, *"My electric bills went up by $50 this year!"* or *"I'm sick of dealing with my utility company!"* Those who do not realize there is a problem will say things like, *"I have no problem paying $150 each month!"* or *"Saving a few dollars a month isn't worth it!"* Discovering such a problem, or "pain point," that a customer has with their current situation is key to selling solar effectively.

The questions you ask during the interview are not only intended to build rapport and form a bond with your customer, but also to understand what pain they are experiencing that solar can alleviate. The sooner you discover the problems that a customer has with how they get electricity, the sooner you can begin appealing to the customer's desire to solve the problem by going solar—this is often referred to as "building the pain."

Before going solar, there is a high probability that they are experiencing one of the following problems:

- **They spend too much money on electricity.**
- **They spend more money on electricity each year.**
- **They would rather spend their hard-earned money on something else.**
- **They don't get any benefits from paying the electric bill each month.**
- **They are unaware of affordable options.**
- **They are making home improvements that will increase their consumption.**

- **They have children coming of age who are using more electricity.**
- **They see many of their neighbors going solar.**
- **They are concerned about the environment.**

While one or more of these problems exist for a given homeowner, they are either unaware of them or have gotten used to them. Paying the electric bill each month has become a deeply ingrained habit for many of us. Asking the right questions during the interview process exposes one or many of the problems above and gives you an opportunity to present a solution by going solar.

As a sales professional, your goal is to *help* customers, so bringing more attention to their "pain" seems a bit counterintuitive. Instead, you can consider the customer's pain points as the "motivation" that drives them to go solar. Once you have discovered what pain your customer is experiencing, it becomes easier to identify their "why"—what is motivating them to go solar.

DISCOVERING KEY MOTIVATORS

Considering how much money a homeowner can save by installing solar panels, it's no wonder why the solar market has exploded in recent years. In some markets, solar virtually sells itself with unparalleled financial returns, but the *key motivators* that compel customers to go solar are not always financial. They are often personal and emotional. In this section, we will explore some of the most common motivators for homeowners and answer the question, "*Why go solar?*"

Key Motivator #1: Saving Money

The financial benefits of solar (Chapter 5) are all related to the first key motivator, which is usually the number one reason for homeowners to go solar: *saving money*. Homeowners across the country spend billions of dollars on electricity each year, so it is no surprise that most solar customers are primarily driven by simply paying less for electricity. To put it plainly: solar power is the simplest way for homeowners to lower their electric bills, and it is the *only* available option for consumers to spend less money on electricity without using less power. Financial returns and savings vary in different markets and depending on the financial options available to customers. *During the interview, discover how important financial benefits are to your customer—and what they hope to achieve.*

Key Motivator #2: Predictability

One of the more understated benefits of solar power is the *predictability* of monthly electric bills after installing solar. Traditional utility bills change each month because households use different amounts of electricity depending on habits such as watching television, going out of town, hosting friends and family, and many other factors. Solar enables homeowners to establish more predictable monthly electric bills—and in some cases, eliminate their electric bills altogether. Solar customers have a better idea of how much they will spend on electricity each month, which allows them to manage their budgets better. *During the interview, discover how important predictability is to your customer.*

Key Motivator #3: Protection from Rising Rates

The retail rates that utility companies charge are complicated, and most homeowners don't have the time to find out exactly what they're paying for. In addition, utility companies gradually increase their rates by various amounts each year, which often goes unnoticed by customers. One of the primary reasons solar is such an effective way to save money is that homeowners can "lock-in" their electric rate and avoid paying more for electricity each year. Even though some homeowners won't immediately start saving hundreds of dollars each month, the amount of money they spend on electricity will continue to go up if they don't do anything. The cost of power for solar customers stays flat while their neighbors' bills continue to rise. *During the interview, discover how concerned your customer is about rising electric bills.*

Key Motivator #4: Energy Independence

The first three key motivators are similar because they relate to the cost of electricity, but customers are also compelled to go solar for emotional reasons. Any homeowner who continues to pay their monthly electric bill will inevitably experience fluctuating monthly bills, rising rates, and unexplained charges. Going solar allows homeowners to gain control over these factors and provides a distinct sense of freedom from the utility company and their unsavory antics. Solar customers who generate some or all of their electricity from rooftop panels continue to rely on utilities for net metering, but going solar provides has a significant advantage: it gives them a choice. Your customers are effectively installing their own power plants, becoming their own power provider, and freeing themselves from monthly payments that don't create any financial value for them—let alone emotional benefits. *During the interview, discover how your customer feels about writing a check to the electric company each month.*

Key Motivator #5: Homeowner Pride

Homeowners always want to be one step ahead of their neighbors when it comes to home improvements and increasing property value. In many cases, once the first solar PV system is installed in a neighborhood, many other nearby houses will follow suit. This is not only because solar is affordable and adds value to the home, but because solar installations increase awareness and contribute to the pride homeowners feel about their most valuable asset. In addition to attracting higher purchase prices and building equity in the home, pulling into the driveway on a sunny day and knowing that solar panels are producing clean and affordable electricity elicits an emotional satisfaction that can feel just as good as saving money. *During the interview, discover how important home value is to your customer.*

Key Motivator #6: Family, Friends, and Social Motivation

Homeowners who get their electricity from renewable energy sources are perhaps the most enthusiastic advocates of solar power. Whether their electricity comes from a renewable energy credit program offered by their utility company, a community solar garden, or from rooftop solar panels, they are eager to tell others about their experience. Most solar companies have *referral programs* because customers who go solar can't help but tell others about how much money they're saving—or that they're powered by clean, renewable energy sources. The direct benefits of going solar are inherently personal, but the experience of investing in renewable energy is one that can be easily shared in the community. *During the interview, discover your customer's relationship with the community and how they share their experiences with others.*

Key Motivator #7: Environmental Protection

In a perfect world, the environmental benefits of solar would be the first item on this list of key motivators. More often than not, the fact that solar is more environmentally friendly than traditional power sources is "icing on the cake" for customers who choose to go solar. The impact of a single rooftop solar PV system is a drop in the bucket when considering the huge environmental challenges we are facing from the overuse of fossil fuels and combustion engines. However, the widespread adoption of solar—especially residential rooftop systems that utilize otherwise wasted surface area—has an important role to play in solving our global environmental crises. Environmental benefits represent a less tangible but equally important benefit that motivates many customers to go solar. *During the interview, discover how important environmental issues are to your customer.*

The interview is the first step in the sales process and is intended to provide the time and space you need to understand what motivates your customer. Choosing to go solar is no minor decision and requires emotional buy-in in addition to financial and logical reasoning. Discovering a homeowner's motivation to go solar is an essential step towards establishing goals with your customer. Building rapport and developing a relationship with your customers is built on genuine interest and trust that begins in the interview.

Everything you learn about your customer allows you to tailor the rest of the sales presentation to your customer and ensure you are recommending the best possible solar solution. You will continue to learn more about your customer throughout the sales process, but the interview cannot go on forever. In the next step of the Solar Sales Method, you will dive deeper into your customer's motivations to establish specific goals that you can help them achieve with solar.

CHECKLIST FOR THE PERFECT INTERVIEW

- ✓ Take a few minutes *before* your sales meeting or introductory phone call to create a list of questions to ask your customer. The more prepared you are to talk to your customer, the more you will be able to learn during the interview.

- ✓ Begin the interview with a fresh sheet of paper—or a blank copy of the *customer account worksheet* provided in the Appendix. Take notes about important details and keep track of your customer's goals and questions.

- ✓ Let the customer do 80 percent of the talking. Give their answers your full attention and show genuine interest in them, listen intently, make eye contact, and take notes to show you are paying attention.

- ✓ Cross-check the list of questions you planned on asking the customer. If you don't have a list, be sure you have an answer to each of the following questions: *who* are you selling to? *Who* are the decision-makers? *What* is important to them? *What* do they expect from solar? *Why* does solar appeal to them?

- ✓ Begin creating a list of potential motivators to help establish what "problem" solar can solve for your customer. Understanding why your customer is interested in solar is key to getting on the right path towards relieving their pain by offering a solution.

CHAPTER 9

STEP 2 - THE VALIDATION: DEMONSTRATE

The first step of the Solar Sales Method focuses on building rapport and getting to know your customers, their personalities, their living situations, and their energy consumption habits. This discovery process unfolds during initial phone calls, emails, and the first few minutes of the sales appointment—whether it is in person, online, or over the phone. Each detail learned about your customer will guide you in recommending the best possible solution. The second step of the Solar Sales Method, *the validation,* is designed to make it clear to the customer that you are presenting their best option.

During the validation, your customer will begin to understand more about *you* and the company you represent while you establish a foundation of goals and motivators to help steer your customer toward making the decision to go solar.

One of the primary goals of the validation is to *demonstrate* that choosing to go solar has many benefits for the customer and explain why they should work with *you*. During this step, you will begin to do a little more talking, around 60 percent, but continue to ask questions and listen to your customers to confirm that you're on the right track and understand them correctly. After all, if you *assume* you know what your customer's goals are, can you *really* be sure that the solution you recommend will achieve those goals?

The answer is simple: come up with a specific goal, or set of goals, with the customer. Accomplishing this allows you to *validate* your customer's need for solar—establishing that there are, in fact, problems to be solved. It also sets the stage to *demonstrate* how solar can provide a solution to meet each one.

The number one objective of the validation step is to establish a specific set of goals—the *goals list*, a hand-written list of goals that your customer wants to achieve. This is the ultimate goal, but there are two parts to the validation: first, demonstrating yourself and your company to *build trust* and confidence. Introducing yourself to customers—who you are, your passion for solar, and your desire to help them improve their lives—and describing the company you represent. The second part is the *goal-setting* process that results in a list of specific motivators, problems, or pain points that will guide you to their best solution.

These two steps can be taken in any order—as long as they follow the interview—depending on your personal style or how the conversation with your customers unfolds. The Solar Sales Method is designed to work for anybody and can be practiced without sacrificing your individuality or your personal style. In fact, your personality will play an important role in your sales career, which is why we begin this section with self-validation.

BUILDING TRUST

As you begin the validation, the conversation will shift a little more to you because going solar is not only about and problem-solving. It is also about your customer trusting *you*. By the end of the interview, your customer has probably told you a lot about themselves, but if you were only doing 20 percent of the talking, then they likely haven't heard much about you. Of course, by now, you have introduced yourself, so the customer knows your name and position, but it is also important to share your story with your customers.

The validation gives you a chance to explain to your customer "*Who am I?*" and "*Why am I here?*" by briefly telling your story and setting the stage for the rest of the sales process. Until your customer trusts you, they will not truly trust what you have to say. We build trust in three simple ways:

1. Telling Your Personal Story

2. Explaining Your Sales Process

3. Following Through on Your Promises

The last item on this list is the most important because proving that you are an honest and high-integrity salesperson is not something you achieve by simply saying, *"I will be honest. Trust me."* Instead, it is something you prove to your customers by living up to your word and showing that you care more about their needs than simply closing a sale. Once you have successfully built a rapport with your potential customers during the interview, it is time to demonstrate who you really are.

Telling Your Personal Story. Behind every sales pitch you will ever present to a customer, one thing will always remain constant: *you.* The interview is intended to help you learn about your customer, but during the validation, you have an opportunity to open up to your customer and show them who you really are. Tell them your "story" and answer two important questions: who are you? Why are you here?

Prepare to tell your story by writing down a paragraph or two about yourself and practice saying it out loud. You may revisit this passage every week or so until you feel it represents you, and over time you will get more comfortable telling it. When you write your story, consider the following questions:

- **What is your "why?"** – *How did you get into solar? Why did you choose this career? What attracted you to the solar industry? Why is this job important to you?*
- **What are your credentials?** – *What qualifies you to sell solar? What did you do to get here? What did you do before this?*

- **What is your strategy? –** *How do you sell solar? What is important to you in this process?*
- **What is your personal history? –** *Where are you from? What do you do in your free time? Do you have any common interests with your customer?*

The more you can bring in your personality, unique skills, and individuality, the more likely you are to rise to the top of your game. Since you have already interviewed your customer, you will likely have identified some areas of common ground, shared interest, or anecdotes to deepen your connection with the customer. Telling your story doesn't always have to be a monologue; it can also be a conversation. People are more likely to connect with a salesperson who is genuine and adaptive to their needs than one reading from a script and focused on selling their product.

Here's an example from a colleague who would give some version of this speech to every customer during the validation:

> *"Before I begin, I'd like to introduce myself, so you know who you're working with. If you choose to go solar, it is important to me that you understand who I am and why I'm here.*
>
> *"I graduated from college with a psychology degree and went into medical sales for fifteen years—at which point I started to feel that I had accomplished little. One day, I was going door-to-door as a volunteer for a political campaign when I ran into a solar canvasser. A week later, I was knocking on doors and setting appointments for solar consultations. A month later, I quit my job in medical sales, and here I am!*

> *"I'm here today because I enjoy helping people discover the benefits of solar, gaining energy independence, saving money, and improving their communities. The most important thing I've learned since I started working in solar is that there is at least one solar solution for everybody. As we work together, I want you to know that my only job is to help you find that solution for you."*

You may have noticed that the word "I" frequently appears in this short speech, and this the only step in the sales process where the focus is on you. So, make it count! The sooner you create your story, and the more you revisit it, the better it will become. More natural, more honest, and as you continue to live the truth of this statement, more *you.*

Your customer is unlikely to sign a contract until they believe that they can put their trust in you—which also means they need to have faith in the company you represent. There is no such thing as a one-man show in the solar industry, so you need to have confidence that the people you work with will meet the expectations you set with your customer.

Part of telling your professional story is explaining why you chose to join the company you work for in the first place. For instance, *"I chose to work with my team because they have the highest installation standards around."* These points can be illustrated by showing how you stand out from the competition. For example:

- Referencing online reviews to show what other customers have enjoyed about working with your company.

- Quantifying how many years of experience your company has installing solar and how many installations they have completed.
- Showcasing the certifications, qualifications, and skills that you and your colleagues have that make you stand out.
- Determining what features and benefits (Chapter 7) your company provides that set you apart from the competition.

The company you represent does not need to stand above and beyond competitors in every category, nor do you need to have a decade of experience in solar sales to demonstrate your ability to help customers. The reason you want to introduce your company while telling your story is that you are not the only person they need to trust. You will display these details about your company in the next step but addressing values and qualifications that you and your company hold answers many questions that naturally come up for customers during the sales process.

Explaining Your Sales Process. The more you share with your customers to prepare them for what is ahead, the fewer surprises they will experience when going solar. Explaining your sales process gives you the opportunity to set expectations with the customer, which begins with *setting the agenda,* not only for the sales appointment but the entire process of going solar. Explaining *your* sales process lets the customer know *what* to expect from you if they choose to go solar as well as *why* they should expect it.

Setting the agenda for the sales meeting means advising your customer on what will occur during the appointment and letting them know what to expect from you. Another important goal of the agenda-setting is to create some structure for the meeting that will help you control the pace of the conversation. An example agenda-setting statement would be something like this:

> *"First, I will tell you about my company, so you know who you'll be working with; next, I will explain how solar works to make sure you understand exactly what solar can do for you. After that, we will take a look at the system I recommend for you. From there, we can discuss the savings and financials as well as the next steps to get to your system installed."*

This step can also occur at the very beginning of your meeting—before the interview—but there are two benefits to waiting until the validation. First, this allows the interview to occur more naturally. It is perfectly fine to include it in the agenda—*"To begin, I'd like to ask you some questions and get to know you so I can be sure to understand your goals and concerns."* However, the more experience you have building rapport with customers, the less you will feel the need to explain that getting to know them is part of the sales process.

The second benefit of waiting until the validation to set the agenda is that it can help you create a better structure for the more informative parts of your sales appointment. This structure will help you stay on course throughout your presentation and maintain control of the conversation with your customer.

Following Through with Your Promises. Building trust with customers isn't accomplished by simply saying, *"trust me."* These are just words, and it takes time to establish trust through action. Letting your customers know that they can trust you is accomplished by following through on your promises, living up to your word, and demonstrating the behaviors that you have told them to expect from you.

The fastest way to build trust with a customer is not by saying what they want to hear but doing what you say you will do. Whether it is finding out the answer to a question they have or special-ordering equipment that they want, you will build trust with your customer through action. Of course, you can't just *tell* your customer that you're going to follow through on your promises, but you can sum up your intentions. For example, explaining your process and goals:

> *"I can't promise that I can find the perfect solution for you, but I can work with you to find the best option for you and your family. I always try to be as transparent as possible, so feel free to ask me any questions that come up at any time."*

During the interview, you developed your customer's story, but the validation process is your chance to relate your own personal "what" and "why" to your customer. Your greatest chance of success is achieved when you and your customer are personally aligned. Then you can validate your role as a guide whose priority is to help them find the best solution available for their needs.

One final note about following through with your promises: you may not always have the luxury of time to prove your trustworthiness to your customer. When you have happy customers that can testify for your honesty and integrity, this provides even more opportunity to *show* that you can be trusted. It is never too early to begin collecting reviews and testimonials from your customers that you can use to promote yourself in the future.

GOAL SETTING

The first part of the validation, building trust with your customer, is an important part of the sales process that takes place over time. Although we focus on building trust during this step in the Solar Sales Method, the most important part of the validation is setting goals to ensure that the rest of your sales process is based on the right information and intentions.

Interviewing your customer teaches you a lot about them, and the more you learn allows you to paint a picture of your customer in your head, allowing you to come up with a list of goals they will *probably* want to achieve. However, taking this one step further ensures that you get *confirmation* that you understand your customer and can present them with the best solution. There are three key steps to successful goal setting: first, set specific goals with the customer to have a reference point for your presentation. Second, writing down their goals and questions so you can keep track of them and return to them when you present the solution. And third, validating solar as the solution they need to achieve their goals.

Setting Specific Goals with Your Customer. Simply asking your customer, *"What are your goals?"* is not the most effective way to begin the sales process because your customer may not know enough about solar to have an answer. However, since you have already interviewed your customer and gained some insight into their situation and potential motivators, you can use this information to create a list of goals together. Establishing your customer's goals is relatively straightforward once you have completed the interview by identifying *self-described problems* or *presumptive problems* from everything you have learned.

Self-described problems are pain points that the customer has described themselves. For example: *"I have noticed that my electric bills are much higher than they were last year,"* or *"I am tired of paying my utility company so much money each month."* From these statements, we can identify two possible goals:

- **Goal #1:** Stop my electric bills from going up.
- **Goal #2:** Achieve some energy independence.

Presumptive problems are pain points that you have intuited from the customer during the interview process. For example, *"I have three children, and the oldest is about to start high school,"* or *"I've always wanted to go to Europe."* While these statements are not related directly to energy consumption, they are directly related to a goal our customer may have:

- **Goal #3:** Keep my electric bills low even if I use more power.
- **Goal #4:** Start saving money for a European vacation.

These examples show how to come up with possible goals for your customer by simply listening for potential "problems" that they are experiencing. To confirm that these are, in fact, goals that are important to your customer, practice repeating what you've heard with questions that may sound something like this: *"You've told me that your electric bills are going up, and with teenagers, you're afraid they will keep going higher. Do I have that right?"* Eliciting a confirmatory answer ensures that you understand the customer, shows that you have been listening, and can help you identify how important each goal is to the customer.

Creating a list of goals based on your customer's problems ultimately gives you the chance to propose solar as a solution. For now, validating a set of goals with the customer allows you to create a written list of goals you and your customer will refer to throughout the sales process.

Creating a List of Goals and Questions. Once you have established your customer's goals, you have the most important thing you need to present a solar solution *for* them. Moving on to *the presentation* before you know what your customer wants to accomplish invariably leads to you presenting a solar solution that you came up with on your own. To avoid this, following the Solar Sales Method will have you create a useful tool for keeping track of goals and questions your customer has about solar. This tool, called the *goals list,* is where you will write down all of the goals your customer has expressed they want to achieve and any questions they have asked you to answer about going solar.

Creating a goals list will help you sell more effectively and help your customer build more confidence and trust in you by showing them that you care about what is important to them. The process of goal setting is not always about getting answers to your questions. Throughout the sales process, your customer will naturally have their own questions. Write down any questions that come up on the goals list so you can be sure to answer them, and you can even ask your customer, *"What questions do you have about solar that I can answer for you today?"* You will inevitably get a variety of responses, from customers who have no specific questions to those who have a long list of inquiries; this will tell you a lot about your customer.

Writing down this list of questions serves as a reminder to address your customers' questions and concerns to not forget about them. It will also help you stay focused and in control of the conversation by simply adding questions to the list as they come up instead of getting off track from your presentation. Perhaps more importantly, the goals list will give you a sense of what you should focus on during your presentation. For example, if your customer asks more questions about price, return on investment, or monthly payments, this might tell you to focus more on financial aspects during your presentation. If they ask more questions about panel efficiency, installation methods, or the timeline of the project, you can adjust your presentation to focus more on the logistical aspects of going solar.

The questions your customer asks will give you a good sense of what they expect to learn from you. As you proceed with your presentation and answer their questions, cross each one off the list as you answer them to reinforce to your customers that you have been listening to what they need, and you are presenting a solution specifically for them.

Validating Solar as the Solution. By creating a goals list with your customer, you will be prepared to knock it out of the park with your presentation. So far, your customer has experienced a sales process that is primarily focused on them, which will make a big difference in their decision of whether solar is right for them. The effort you have put into getting to know your customer makes it possible to establish a relationship built on trust. Presenting a solution that your customer understands is *specifically* designed for them instills a sense of understanding and control.

Selling solar effectively begins with developing a certain level of trust and connection with your customers, and it ends with presenting a personalized solution that the customer believes is best for them. As you complete the validation, reviewing the goals list with your customer before your presentation gives you the chance to explain how solar is, in fact, the solution that they need to meet their goals. This validation can simply be a general statement: *"From what you've told me, installing solar is going to help you lower your bills and save up for that European vacation because you'll be buying less electricity from your utility company."* In the next steps of the Solar Sales Method, your customer will learn exactly *how* and *why* solar is the right choice and the only way they can achieve their goals.

CHECKLIST FOR THE PERFECT VALIDATION

✓ Practice your story. Write down two or three paragraphs about yourself to make improvements and eventually have a well-practiced personal story that is interesting and informative for your customers—and sounds natural.

✓ Set an Agenda. Most of your sales appointments should have a similar flow if you are following the Solar Sales Method. However, you have your own personal style, and every customer is different, so creating an agenda for each meeting will help you make the most of the time you spend with your customer.

✓ Create a *goals list* with at least one primary goal, and ideally, two or three secondary goals that the customer has specifically said are important to them. In addition, make a list of any questions the customer would like answered. Unlike the customer account worksheet that is for your own notes and records, this goals list is something you will reference with the customer throughout the sales process.

✓ Don't be afraid to continue the interview, continuing to focus on listening to your customer and getting them to talk about their thoughts, feelings, and opinions as much as possible. This will give you more time to come up with the best possible solution.

CHAPTER 10

STEP 3 – THE PRESENTATION: DISPLAY

So far, we've discussed the history of solar power, how PV systems work, and the industry trends that brought solar to the mainstream. We learned about different kinds of jobs, career growth opportunities, and where to apply yourself to make the most of your skills and abilities. We covered many of the features, benefits, and motivators that drive people to go solar. Finally, we started learning how to develop a strong connection with customers to understand their needs. So, how do we apply all of this to selling solar?

In the third step of the Solar Sales Method, *the presentation,* you will begin actively presenting solar to your customers, relating all of the information, opportunities, and benefits you have learned about. The primary goal of this step is to *display* solar as the best option your customer has to achieve the goals that are important to them.

Selling solar effectively is not achieved by manipulating or convincing customers that the benefits of solar outweigh the cost. The Solar Sales Method is an effective and integrity-based approach to sales that will help you guide your customers toward making a decision that is in *their* best interest—whatever their goals may be. People don't always buy things based on logic. Many of us end up buying things we don't need because of impulse, instinct, or other emotional reasons; however, going solar is a large investment and generally does not occur instinctively. Your role as a solar sales professional is to present solar to your customers so that it guides them toward a choice that will improve their quality of life. It will save their hard-earned dollars and achieve the goals you have identified together—meeting their logical, financial, and emotional needs.

The first two steps of the Solar Sales Method focused on identifying the customers' needs, which allows you to come up with the best solution *for the customer*. The presentation follows a specific formula, but you must also take into account what your customer already knows about solar—and what they don't know—while focusing on their goals, questions, concerns, and the aspects of solar that are most appealing to them. This keeps customers engaged and reinforces the reasons they are speaking to you in the first place: to help them find the best solution for their home.

The presentation is guided by a *pitch book*—a series of informative slides to guide the conversation—which can be printed in a folder, shown digitally on a device, or presented as an online slideshow. For the first time in the Solar Sales Method, you will take the microphone and do the majority of the talking, presenting five key topics:

1. About Your Company
2. How Solar Power Works
3. Presenting the Problem
4. Electric Bill Review
5. Presenting the Solution

By the end of the presentation, your customer will have *all* the information they need about going solar, so when you present their solar PV system, they can make an informed decision. Your company will most likely provide you with a pitch book made up of a series of slides that guide the presentation, but if not, you can create your own. This section includes "Slide Suggestions" that you can use to develop your own presentation deck—or to enhance the one you have been provided.

ABOUT YOUR COMPANY: ADDRESSING THE "WHO"

The presentation begins, once again, by developing a foundation of trust with your customer by returning to the question, *"Who are you?"* You have already told your personal story—including why you chose to work with your company. Now it is time to show clearly and definitively *who* your customer will be working with. It might seem like overkill, but going solar is a commitment that could last over thirty years, so your customer must have confidence in the people behind their investment.

The more developed your company's brand is, the more experience they have, or the longer they have been in business, the more likely you will have a plethora of information to include in this section. However, the first step in the presentation is not simply to list the accolades of the company you work for. It is to show your customer who they're dealing with, and what makes you and your company stand out—*Slide Suggestion: "Company Profile."* The company's profile slide should include details about the organization, such as:

- **What year was the company founded?**
- **What markets does the company operate in?**
- **What does the company specialize in?**
- **What relevant acclaims or accreditations does it hold?**
- **What warranties does the company offer?**
- **What unique partnerships or affiliations does the company have?**

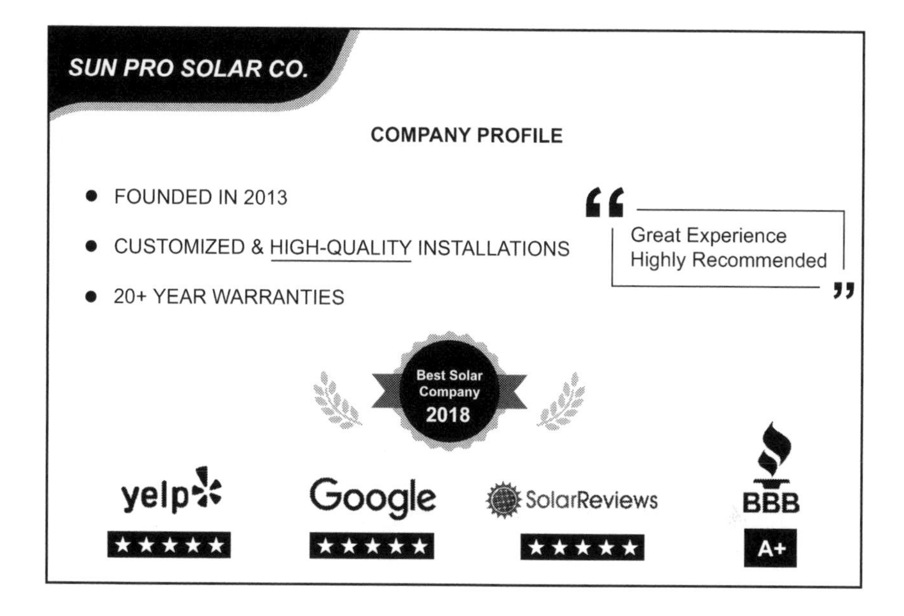

Fig.15 Company Profile Slide

As you present your company, let the slide speak for itself while you verbally describe the most relevant and important features of your company to your customer: "*You said you wanted to make sure you'd be taken care of if anything went wrong, we offer one of the most competitive warranties in this market.*" In the previous step, you should have already described why *you* chose to work for your company. Now it is your opportunity to explain why your *customer* will want to do the same. In other words, effectively presenting your company allows you to show the customer some proof that the system you install will live up to expectations and the promises you are making.

The goal of the company slide is to create a connection between your company and high-quality solar installations. Once you have set this precedent, your customer will be much more likely to envision themselves working with you—because they choose *quality* when they buy—as you move on to the next slide in the presentation: explaining how solar PV systems work.

HOW SOLAR POWER WORKS: ADDRESSING THE "HOW"

One of the challenges to selling solar effectively is answering the question, *"How does solar work?"* over and over to your customers. With experience, you will get better at describing how solar panels work, but you'll also run the risk of oversimplifying solar technology as you get more comfortable with the subject. Occasionally you will meet customers who have already looked into solar or tell you they already know how solar works—but still, this step must not be overlooked.

Part of getting to know your customer is determining how much they understand about solar in general, but also what details are important to them. It is up to you to determine how much time to dedicate to solar technology and how much detail to go into during the presentation. Even with the most informed customers, this allows you to display to your customers that *you* have a deep knowledge of what you're selling and that you understand which aspects of the technology are most important to *them*.

It's also important to discuss how solar works in some detail during the presentation because the industry is constantly changing, from the technology available to rebates and net metering rules. You must ensure your customer is up-to-speed on how everything will work for them in their home and with their utility company.

Presenting how solar works begins with an overview of a solar PV system—*Slide Recommendation: How Solar PV Systems Work*—which depicts key components and how they work together to deliver electricity to the customer. This is your opportunity to explain solar in terms that your customer can understand and draw attention to the details that they have expressed interest in or have questions about.

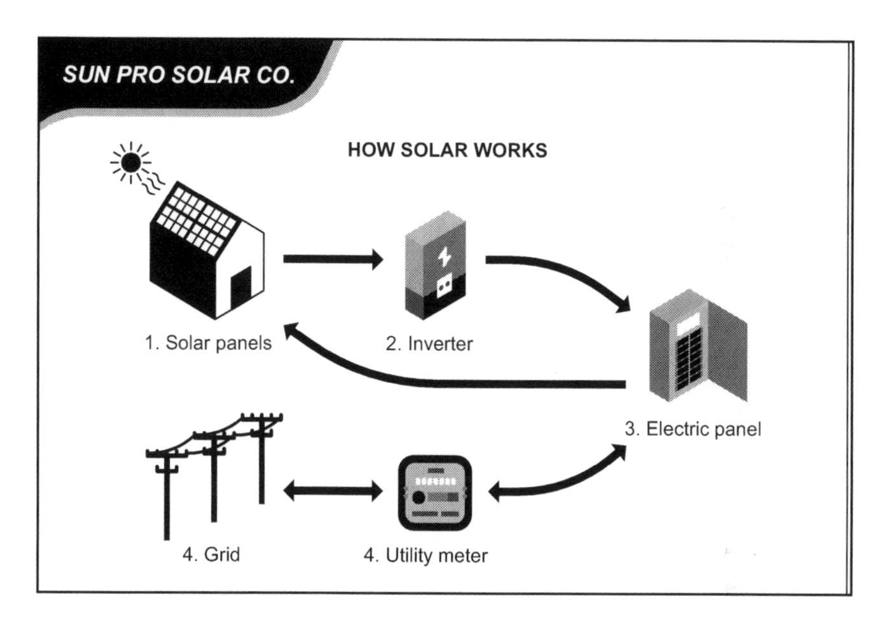

Fig.16 How Solar Works Slide

A simple visual that shows the flow of electricity from one component of the system to the next provides an opportunity to explain each part of the system, its role in producing electricity, and how exactly a solar PV system connects to the customer's home. Most customers know that solar panels will be installed on their roof, so this part of the presentation is primarily intended to describe how the panels connect to the inverter, electrical panel, and utility meter to provide them with the electricity they need.

Once you have addressed the components and how they work together, the next step in the presentation is answering the question, *"What happens to the electricity I generate?"* Understanding solar equipment is the first step to understanding how solar works. The second step is understanding net metering—*Slide Recommendation: How Net Metering Works*—and explaining how your customers get to take advantage of the power they produce when they aren't home or at night when the sun is not shining.

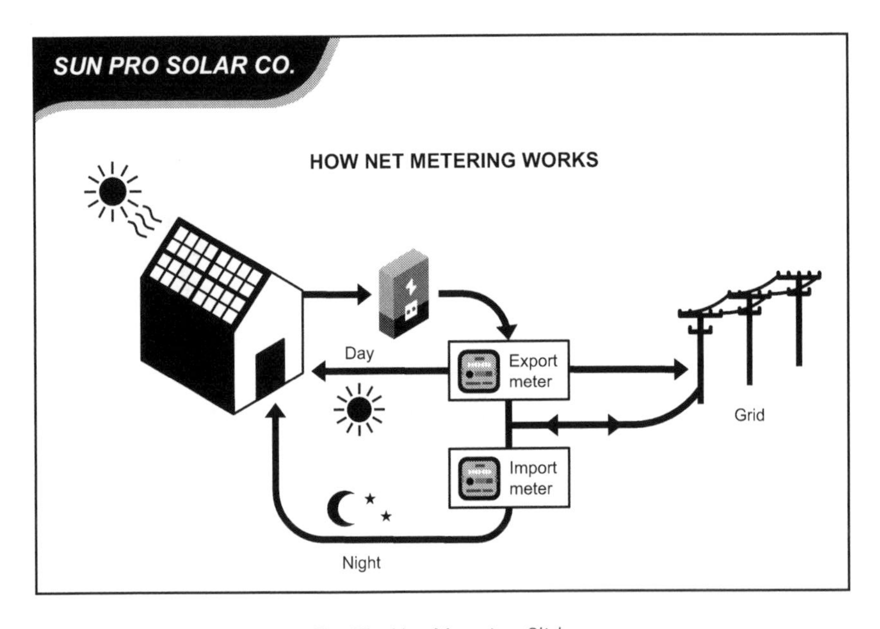

Fig.17. Net Metering Slide

Net metering is one of the most important subjects for many customers because it explains *how* the power they generate on their roof is available to them when they need it. Many questions, concerns, and objections from customers originate from misunderstanding net metering. As you gain experience selling solar, learning to describe net metering so that customers understand it will be crucial for your success. Once your customer understands net metering, they can truly begin to appreciate solar as a solution to their problems and a means of achieving their goals.

PRESENTING THE PROBLEM: ADDRESSING THE "WHY"

The presentation is your chance to put solar power on display so your customers fully understand what they are installing on their home. By this point, you have identified specific goals for your customer and should have a pretty good idea of which features and benefits appeal to them the most. This means you don't have to explain everything about solar or list off every possible benefit. Instead, set the stage for the story you want to tell your customer, which answers the question, *"Why should I go solar?"*

One reason your customers will decide to go solar is to achieve the goals you set with them in the previous step of the Solar Sales Method. Another reason is to solve a problem for your customer—whether they know they have one or not—by identifying opportunities to improve their quality of life with solar. The presentation is your chance to display solar as a way to achieve what they care most about—whether it is lower electric costs, more predictable bills, energy independence, or one of the many other reasons.

By this step, you have identified at least one specific concern your customer has about their current situation and established at least one goal. If not, you may need to go back to the interview step. Even if your customer has acknowledged they have a problem, they may be comfortable with it—*"I only pay $100 a month!"*—which is why clarifying the problems your customer has if they stick with their utility company is a critical step of the presentation. You can tailor the presentation specifically to each customer and their individual motivations, but in the Solar Sales Method, we address one issue that is likely to affect each one of your customers: *rising electric bills*. No matter where your customers live or what utility company supplies their power, the cost of electricity will inevitably continue rising.

If your customer does not believe they have a problem, they are less likely to invest in a solution. Whether they are very concerned about their electric bills or feel comfortable paying them each month, an ever-increasing electric bill is a problem that provides all customers with an opportunity. Explaining the rising cost of electricity provides customers with a choice: stick with the utility company and continue to pay more for power each month or go solar and take control of their electric bills—*Slide Recommendation: The Cost of Electricity.*

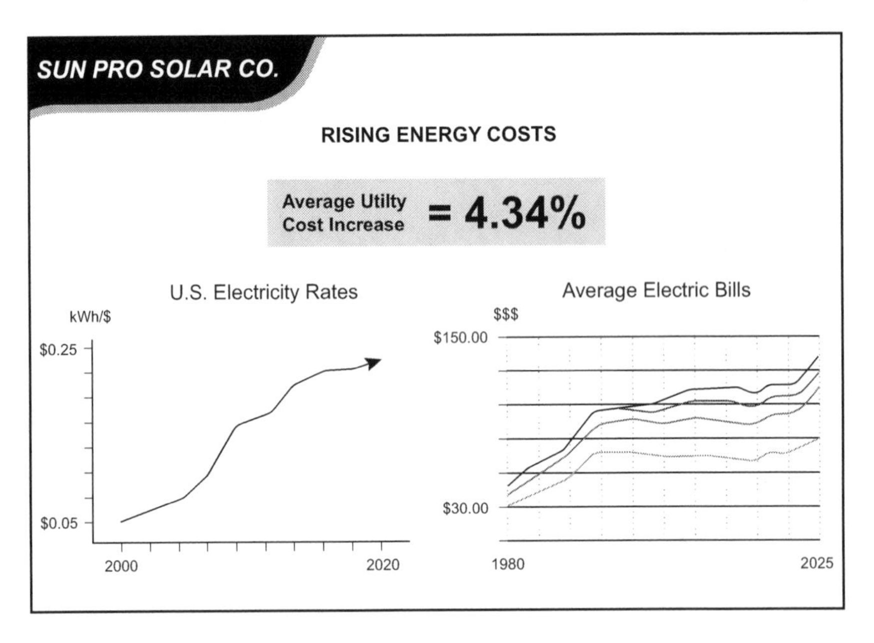

Fig.18. Rising Energy Costs Slide

Showing customers that they have been paying more and more for electricity over the years provides an opportunity to dig into a problem that just about anybody can understand. Ask your customers how they feel about paying their electric bill each month and what they think about paying increasingly more for the same service. Some homeowners who have lived in their homes for a long time are more likely to have noticed the gradual—or sometimes rapid—rise of their electric bills. New homeowners or a customer who moved to a different utility territory are less likely to have this experience, but nonetheless, it is possible to demonstrate.

Electricity prices are regulated at many levels, and residential rates are monitored by Public Utility Commissions (PUC) and other agencies. Nonetheless, utility companies are constantly finding ways to raise rates and residential electricity rates in the U.S. are increasing each year. Until utility companies are forced to find alternative revenue sources, there is no reason to expect this trend to come to an end. In other words, utility companies will continue to sell electricity at the highest possible price to cover their costs and maintain their control of the energy industry.

If there is a single, universal benefit to going solar that appeals to each one of your customers, it is protection from rising rates. Solar provides customers with an opportunity—a choice—to take control of their electric bills. You have identified yourself and your company as a high-integrity outfit, explained how solar works, and now you have identified a clear opportunity for your customer to take control of their electricity spending. Next, you'll get a little more personal by digging deeper into a subject that most customers do not understand while examining a copy of their electric bill.

ELECTRIC BILL REVIEW: DIGGING DEEPER INTO THE "WHY"

Utility companies charge customers a *retail rate* for the electricity they consume, which is determined by many factors beyond their desire to be profitable. Retail rates are not only calculated from the cost of electricity generation and transmission—the *wholesale rate*—they also cover the utility companies operating costs. This includes everything from investments in expanding their service territories, keeping the electric grid functioning, dispatching employees to repair outages, and all of the overhead costs associated with running a business.

By the time your customer's electric bill is calculated, the amount of money they are paying for electricity each month is often *more* for grid maintenance and business operations than the actual price of electricity generation. Utility companies try to maximize their revenue by generating electricity from the cheapest fuel sources—primarily coal and natural gas. However, the increasing cost of maintaining the grid leads to revenue shortages that the utility companies make up for by increasing retail rates for customers.

The *bill review* is an important part of the presentation because it gives you one more chance to expose another common problem that customers have: they don't *really* know what they're paying for each month. Electric bills are determined by a set of charges, called *tariffs*, that are used to calculate the total electric bill. These tariffs define the various charges that a customer faces when they consume electricity and fall into two categories: *electricity charges* and *delivery charges*. Depending on the utility company, a list of these charges can be found on the electric bill, although some companies will not provide such details.* Reviewing the customer's electric bill is best with an actual copy of the electric bill, but this step in the presentation can also be performed using a sample electric bill from the customer's utility company—*Slide Recommendation: Understanding Your Electric Bill.*

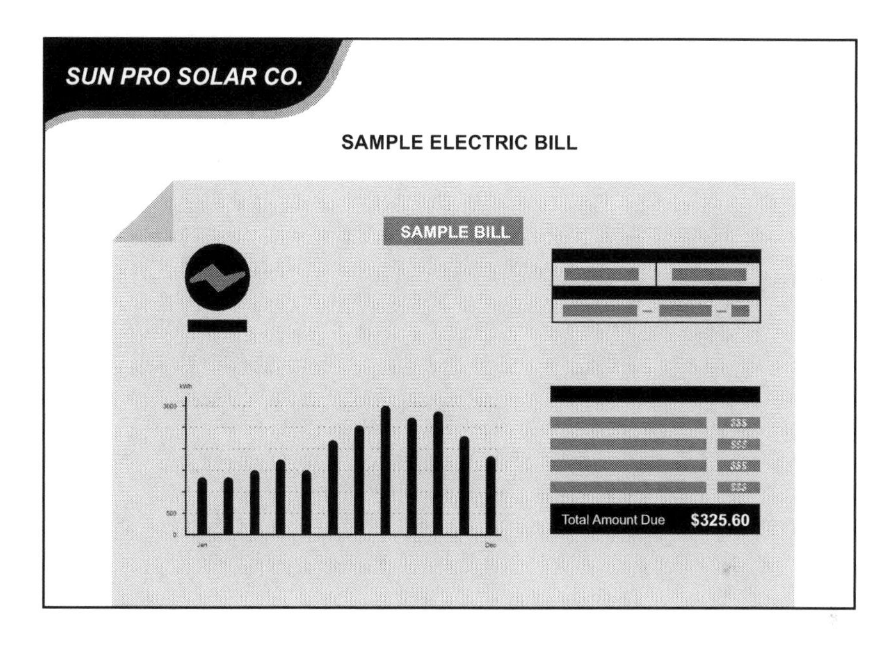

Fig.19. Sample Electric Bill Slide

Describing your customer's electric bill can get complicated, but this illustrates that utility companies have little incentive to help their customers understand exactly what they are being charged for. In addition to the list of tariffs and charges, some utility companies increase the rates their customers pay when they reach a certain threshold of consumption during a billing period, at certain times of day, or during specific months of the year, called *tiered rates.*

---

* If the electricity char ges and delivery charges are not provided in detail on the electric bill, you will find a complete list of tarif fs on the utility company's website.

Tiered rate structures differ greatly between utilities, from the number of tiers to how much rates increase between tiers and whether they are imposed daily or seasonally as summer and non-summer rates. A similar pricing structure that is also becoming more common in residential markets is *time-of-use rates*. This mechanism is different mainly because different rates are charged and will vary throughout each day, often appearing more complicated and changing hourly or even at fifteen-minute intervals.

No matter how a utility company calculates their customer's electric bills, reviewing the charges with your customer is an opportunity to illustrate what they are currently paying for. This will help you move toward presenting solar as a solution to your customer, as they will begin to understand exactly what charges they will be able to avoid by going solar.

PRESENTING THE SOLUTION: ADDRESSING THE "WHAT"

Selling solar effectively is not just a matter of coming up with the right solar PV system and describing the features and benefits. To ensure your customer is ready to make the decision to go solar, you must prepare them by establishing that the customer understands they have a problem that needs solving.

A colleague of mine once described the process of selling solar as walking the customer down a hallway lined with open doors, closing each one along the way until you have reached the end. Each door represents a question, concern, or issue that needs to be addressed before the customer can confidently make the decision to go solar. By the time you reach the end of the Solar Sales Method, if your customer still has questions, concerns, or objections, it means there are still doors that remain open, and you still have work to do.

With the final topic of the presentation, we close one more door by presenting solar as *a solution* and describe what it accomplishes for our customers. Before we present the customer with the solar PV system that we recommend for their home, we tell them a quick story by comparing their current situation to the future. Do this by comparing your customer's electric bill *before solar* with their bill *after solar* to illustrate exactly how their situation will change if they choose to go solar—*Slide Recommendation: Bill Comparison.*

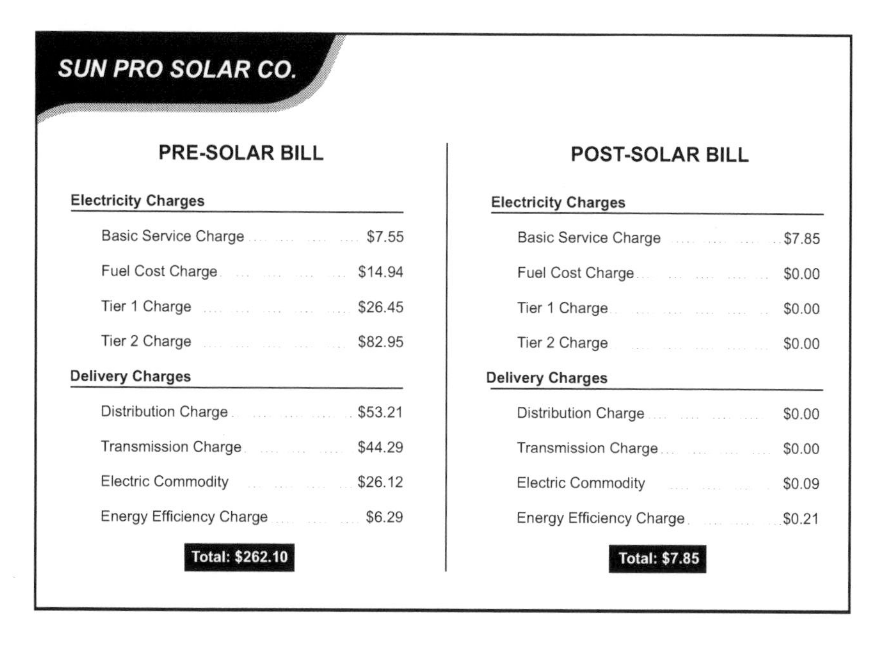

SUN PRO SOLAR CO.

PRE-SOLAR BILL		POST-SOLAR BILL	
Electricity Charges		**Electricity Charges**	
Basic Service Charge	$7.55	Basic Service Charge	$7.85
Fuel Cost Charge	$14.94	Fuel Cost Charge	$0.00
Tier 1 Charge	$26.45	Tier 1 Charge	$0.00
Tier 2 Charge	$82.95	Tier 2 Charge	$0.00
Delivery Charges		**Delivery Charges**	
Distribution Charge	$53.21	Distribution Charge	$0.00
Transmission Charge	$44.29	Transmission Charge	$0.00
Electric Commodity	$26.12	Electric Commodity	$0.09
Energy Efficiency Charge	$6.29	Energy Efficiency Charge	$0.21
Total: $262.10		**Total: $7.85**	

Fig.20. Pre-Solar Bill vs. Post-Solar Bill Slide

Reviewing your customer's electric bill illustrates what the electric company is actually charging them each month. Comparing it to a post-solar bill shows what charges they can avoid once they have gone solar. The comparison puts your customer at the center of the story you have been telling and provides concrete evidence that shows what solar can actually do for them. Once you have reached this point, you have presented yet another piece of evidence that the solar PV system you are recommending is a solution for the problems they are experiencing—as well as the means to achieve their goals.

Once you have reached this point, it is natural that your customer may still have some doubts about going solar. This is a good place to check-in, ask your customer if they have any more questions, and refer to your goals list to see if there are any questions that you have yet to answer—and cross off all of the questions you've gotten to so far. If the customer does not have any more questions and they have expressed interest in seeing what their solar solution will look like, it's time to move on to the next step and present the solar solution that you recommend.

CHECKLIST FOR THE PERFECT PRESENTATION

- ✓ Spend a few minutes relating your personal story to the company you represent—*Why you chose to work for your company? What do you enjoy about it?* This helps your customer feel more comfortable about working with you and gives them a chance to think about their own personal thoughts and concerns about going solar.

- ✓ Before your sales meeting, do some research about the utility company that supplies your customer's electricity—*How much do they charge for electricity? How much have rates risen in past years?* Use this data to create a compelling visual supplement to explain their current situation—particularly, that the cost of electricity is rising.

- ✓ Before your sales meeting, ask for a copy of your customer's electric bill or acquire an example electric bill from your customer's utility company. Familiarize yourself with the rate structures and the charges that are listed on their bill.

CHAPTER 11

STEP 4 – THE SOLUTION: DECIDE

Counterintuitively, when the topic of sales comes up, the first thing that often comes to mind is the *end* of the sales process—the contract signing or the transaction that consummates a sale. Of course, closing a sale is a critical step in the process—and without it, there *is* no sale—but salespeople tend to focus too much on the outcome of the sales process, which detracts from the more important and enjoyable work leading up to the sale.

Top performers in the solar industry are not simply the best at closing customers. They also excel at the process that leads to a signed contract. To be more specific, the best solar sales professionals spend more time training to identify customer's needs and create emotional buy-in than practicing closing techniques. This ensures your customer is clear about *what* they are purchasing, which will help them understand *why* the solution you present to them is their best option. This takes place in the fourth step of the Solar Sales Method, *the solution*.

The primary goal of the solution is to help your customer *decide* whether to go solar by presenting their best option based on the information you've gathered. The structure of the Solar Sales Method until this point ensures that you have identified what is most important to your customer so you can present your *best* recommendation—the solution they will be most likely to choose.

In many ways, the solution is the culmination of the sales cycle, where the information you have collected about your customer is applied. Instead of focusing on identifying problems and questions, you will begin offering solutions and detailed answers. In this step, you will present the solar PV system you recommend, show how it will achieve your customer's goals, and address any remaining questions and concerns. By the end of this step, you will bring your customer to a decision point—one way or another.

THE PROPOSAL

The solution is guided by a *solar proposal* that you must generate for each of your customers. The proposal is a document that includes all of the detailed information your customer will be eager to hear about, from the cost of their PV system and the payback period to production estimates and equipment details. Presenting the solution is one of the most anticipated steps in the sales cycle—perhaps next to the day their solar panels begin producing electricity. For this reason, it is very important to ensure that you have taken the time to present the *best* option for your customer.

Throughout your career in solar sales, one of the most important skills you will develop is using the *proposal tool* your company provides to create quotes, proposals, and contracts for customers. There are many different versions of these tools, from proprietary software developed in-house to online tools available by subscription, but they all serve the same purpose of designing PV systems and creating solar proposals. The more familiar you are with these tools, and the more you practice with them, the better you will become at presenting the best solution to your customers.

Many solar sales professionals create proposals for their customers before they show up at the sales appointment. Upon arriving at their customer's house, they dive straight into the proposal, explaining how simple and wonderful solar is and convincing the customer that they have designed the best possible PV system for them. Some solar sales professionals are successful in this approach because they are persistent in their efforts. However, you may already see why this strategy is ineffective—the Solar Sales Method is designed to save your time and energy that would otherwise be wasted on persistence, follow-up, and persuasion.

Everything you learn ahead of your first meeting with a potential customer helps you design a solar PV system and arrive with an attractive proposal. From the very first interaction with customers, you begin gathering information about them—their usage data, details of their home and family life, insights into their lifestyle. This information builds a database that you can use to come up with the best possible solar solution for their needs. However, no matter how much information you collect before meeting with a customer, the needs and goals you established during the interview and validation are critical to developing the right solution.

Designing a solar PV system requires specific information, such as the customer's historical usage and a satellite image of their home, but designing the right system requires familiarity and understanding that is best gathered in conversation. The more practice you have with your proposal tool software, the more quickly you can tweak and update your solar proposal in the field as you get to know your customer. Ultimately you want to present your customer with *one solution*—the *best* solution—that you have come up with based on all of the information you have learned so far. The more experience you have with the Solar Sales Method, the more likely you will be to present the solution that best fits your customer's goals and desires.

Presenting a customer with too many options can negatively affect your sales process, which becomes evident in three ways:

1. **Paralysis by Analysis.** Showing customers too many system designs, equipment selections, prices, and financing options can cause them to hesitate when coming to a decision because they're afraid of making the wrong choice.

2. **All or Nothing.** Showing customers too many purchasing options—such as a cash option with faster payback and

greater savings than the loan or PPA they can afford—can make the best option for them look comparatively underwhelming. This can cause customers to pass on going solar at all because they're unwilling to settle for the second-best option.

3. **Losing Their Way**. Showing customers various options may initially seem like a good way to give them the freedom to make their own choice, but there is a lot of information to digest. This may cause customers to feel overwhelmed and give them the impression that you have not been paying attention to what they are looking for.

Presenting your customers with a single option helps avoid these downfalls and has the added benefit of keeping your customer emotionally engaged. Furthermore, presenting a single option does not prevent you from making additional tweaks and changes to reach a better solution for the customer. The solution is your chance to show your customer that their goals are being met as you explain to the customer *what* you have chosen and *why*: *"The reason I have come up with this solution is because of what you have told me is most important to you. To reach your goals, this is the solution I recommend."*

The amount and quality of the information in a solar proposal will vary depending on which tool you are using, but the following topics are highly important to homeowners considering solar. How much detail you go into and the time you spend on each section should be determined by your customer and what they find most appealing and important.

Like the presentation, the proposal will have you doing most of the talking as you present your recommendation to the customer. Nevertheless, you can keep your customer involved and engaged, asking them questions and making sure they are following everything and understand how it relates to their goals and needs. If more questions come up, answer them as they arise whenever possible or add them to your list to address later.

The proposal you create for each of your customers will include a lot of data and information, but there are three key subjects to address in the solution. As you go over each of the following subjects, you will be showing your customer exactly what they need to understand about going solar.

1. The PV System: Design, Summary, and Performance
2. The Cost: Pricing and Net Investment
3. The Benefits: Payments, Savings, and Payback

THE PV SYSTEM: DESIGN, SUMMARY, AND PERFORMANCE

The first step to presenting the solution is showing your customer the *design* of the PV system that you are recommending for their home. The design summary includes a digital rendering showing the layout of the solar panels on the customer's roof, how many panels (the size of the system), and what kind of equipment will be installed.

Naturally, presenting the solution begins with providing details that explain exactly what the customer is getting, which includes the *performance* of the system—how much power they will be able to generate, their electric bill offsets, and what they can expect over time.

PV System Design: Solar PV systems are designed to maximize power production for customers because higher-performing solar PV systems are better investments. Of course, it is not always as simple as putting panels where they will perform best. Architectural restrictions, surrounding trees, utility poles, or other structures that cast a shadow, and the customer's aesthetic preferences all come into play. Nevertheless, presenting your design to the customer should emphasize power production over all other factors—*"The reason I am recommending you install the panels here is to maximize your power production and make the most of your investment."*

It is common for homeowners to be concerned about the location of their solar panels, so discussing any aesthetic concerns *before* you present your recommendation helps avoid places where the customer doesn't want solar panels—*"I chose this location for the solar panels because you mentioned not wanting solar panels on the front of your house. How does this look?"*

It is not always possible to install panels where the customer wants them, but it is important to show that you have put their concerns into consideration even if you cannot live up to them—*"I know you were hoping to install the panels on the back of your house, but that will greatly affect your benefits from going solar. Are you okay with putting the panels here?"*

The PV System Summary: The system summary provides some-general details of the solution you are recommending. Specifically, it will describe how many panels, the size of the system, and the electricity offset your customer can achieve. Quickly reviewing the summary should not raise any additional objections or concerns if you have effectively understood the customer's needs and preferences. Instead, the summary allows you to reiterate *why* you have designed the system this way—*"A system this size will produce 106 percent of your power consumption to meet your goal of offsetting your entire electric bill."*

In addition to system size, the proposal summary should also provide some details about the equipment you are recommending, particularly the solar panels and inverter, which will give you a chance to explain the reasoning behind your choice of this equipment—*"These are our most popular solar panels and have a very competitive warranty, and your system is designed with micro-inverters to maximize production."*

Proposal summaries often include an overview of utility rate increases, avoided utility costs, environmental benefits such as avoided CO2 emissions, and the performance estimates of the system. Depending on your customer, you may choose to go into more detail about some of these topics, but one of the more important details is the production estimate you are presenting.

PV System Performance: The design you come up with your customer is intended to maximize power production, which leads to the important topic of system performance. This means going into detail about *production estimates* and *electric bill offsets*. As you learned, production guarantees are not very common in the solar industry (Chapter 7), so helping your customer feel comfortable with the estimates you are presenting is critical to selling solar effectively. System production is calculated in kWh, so describing production estimates as a percentage of their current electric bill helps put it in terms they can understand—*"The system I'm recommending is estimated to produce around 6500 kWh each year, which means you can offset 98 percent of your electricity needs."*

Helping your customer understand how production estimates are determined is important for two reasons. First, they should know that performance estimates are generated by NREL's PVWatts tool, which takes into account all details of their location, including historical weather data, the equipment you are using, and the layout of the solar panels on their roof. If your customer knows *how* this estimate is calculated, you'll have an easier time explaining power production—*"I have been conservative with my estimates, so I am confident that you can expect to produce* at least *this much electricity from your PV system."*

The second reason to help your customer understand production estimates is to maintain an edge in competitive situations. For example, your competitors are showing significantly higher production estimates from a smaller or similar PV system. Your customer is likely to understand and appreciate that your estimates are realistic when they can compare them to the inflated numbers of your competition—*"I try to be as realistic as possible with my estimates, based on the details of your home and the system I am recommending, so you can be certain that your system will live up to your expectations. My goal is to under-promise and over-deliver."*

THE COST: PRICING AND NET INVESTMENT

One of the foremost questions on your customer's mind will inevitably be, *"How much will it cost?"* As a solar sales professional, delaying your answer to this question is one of the more challenging aspects of effective sales. Until you have all the information you need, it is difficult to provide your customer with an accurate price. Only after you've generated your customer's proposal can you answer their question, *"How much will I spend?"* and more importantly, *"How much will I save?"*

Solar System Price: The price of a solar PV installation is determined by much more than the solar panels, inverters, and racking systems. Choosing premium, top-of-the-line equipment will raise the price for customers, but the cost of a solar installation is also affected by the customer's roof, the construction of their home, how many panels they need, and where the panels are installed—in addition to some other intangible factors. As you present the cost, it is helpful to remind customers that they are seeing the price for a turnkey installation—*"This price includes all of the equipment, labor, installation, permits, fees, and any other costs that will be incurred to complete your project, so there will be no hidden charges or other payments needed from you."*

When describing the price, it is helpful to reiterate that solar projects are designed specifically for each customer and their home. Many different factors affect pricing, such as the type of roofing on their home, the steepness of their roof, and how many places the solar panels are installed. Addressing the extra costs associated with your customer's project, called *adders*, shows your customer that you've taken everything into account—*"This prices includes the cost of installing panels on your cement-tile roof, which requires more expensive racking. I've included all of these costs so there won't be any surprises later."*

Net Investment: All of the costs mentioned above add up to the *total price* of a solar PV installation, but this price does not include the tax credits, incentives, or rebates that are subtracted from the total to calculate your customer's *net investment*. Presenting this figure is relatively straightforward—*"Once you receive the federal tax credit and state incentives,* this *is this total amount that you will have invested in your solar project. We use this number to calculate the payback on your investment."*

The financial benefits of going solar are directly related to the price and the financial investment that your customer will need to make. However, presenting the price of a solar installation is relatively straightforward compared to understanding benefits and then payback on a solar investment. In other words, your customer must understand that they can *save* tens of thousands of dollars by going solar, which will prepare them to *invest* so much money in solar. Rather than spending too much time discussing price, it's best to confirm that your customer understands the number they are seeing so you can move on to the benefits—*"Does this number make sense to you?"*

THE BENEFITS: PAYMENTS, SAVINGS, AND FINANCIAL BENEFITS

Presenting price to your customer is a pivotal moment, and much of the anticipation building throughout the solar sales is leading to this point. You may want to get to the price as quickly as possible. After all, it is probably your customer's number one question. But following each of the steps in the Solar Sales Method is critical to preparing your customer for a five-figure investment in solar. It will also get your customer excited about the *savings and benefits* they will experience by going solar.

Solar Payments: As you know, there are many ways to finance a solar project, each with a different impact on the payments a customer makes on their project. Addressing the payments section of your proposal can be a challenging step and often brings up some objections for customers who have set their expectations too high or simply want to eliminate their electric bill when this is not possible. Your customer's solar payments will relate specifically to how your customer chooses to finance their system, which illustrates the importance of presenting *one* option to your customer to keep things simple.

Cash purchases offer the simplest explanation of solar payments—*"Once your solar panels are installed, you won't have to make any payments except for any additional electricity you draw from the utility and your monthly service fee."* However, if cash is not an option, avoid making the comparison, so your customer doesn't feel like they are missing out on greater savings. The key to explaining solar payments is twofold: comparing post-solar costs to the cost of doing nothing, and comparing the customer's fixed solar payments to the ever-increasing utility bill—*"Your solar payment of $110 per month is 8 percent less than what you're currently paying. Unlike your utility bill, this will be the same each month until you've paid off your solar loan. At that point, you won't be paying for electricity anymore!"*

Solar Savings: The financial benefits your customers receive from solar begin and end with *savings.* While there are a few ways customers can generate "revenue" or "earnings" from solar—tax credits, rebates, feed-in tariffs—the bulk of the financial benefits from going solar come from paying *less* for electricity—*"By going solar, you will save over $30,000 on electricity. Here's how that works."*

Solar proposals often include projections of solar savings over a twenty-year period, which is the standard length of a PPA and a typical term for solar panel warranties.* There are two key ways to helping your customer understand their savings. The first is by focusing on the *annual utility rate increase* they can avoid with solar—*"Today, you are paying almost $2,000 each year for electricity, but utility rates are going up around 4 percent each year. That means in ten years, you'll be paying nearly $3,000 each year, and in twenty years, you'll be paying more than double!"*

Regardless of how your customer pays for their solar project, their utility bill will *decrease* once they have gone solar, which is the simplest way to calculate solar savings:

OLD UTILITY BILL - NEW UTILITY BILL = SOLAR SAVINGS

One of the challenges with presenting solar savings is encouraging your customer to look beyond their monthly savings in the short term—saving a few dollars a month is not as motivating as the big numbers shown by annual savings and twenty-year savings. The second way to illustrate the true savings from solar is illustrating the *price of electricity* your customer pays to their utility compared to

---

* Solar panels can generate electricity for over thirty years, so it is becoming more common to see twenty-five-year and thirty-year saving estimates

how much they will pay with solar—"*Over the next twenty years, the average rate your utility company will charge you for electricity is $0.16 per kWh, compared to $0.07 per kWh from the solar PV system I am recommending.*"

The most important part of presenting solar savings is making sure your customer understands the numbers you are showing them. Your proposal will likely include many figures, graphs, and charts that can help your customer visualize the numbers you are describing to them. Ensure they do not have any remaining doubts or questions about their potential savings by asking clarifying questions, and make sure to draw a clear connection between their net investment and their net solar savings—"*The cost of this investment is $30,900, which will save you more than $43,000 over the next twenty-five years. How does that sound to you?*"

Financial Benefits: The financial benefits of solar are primarily calculated from electric bill savings, but as you know, there are many kinds of financial rewards for customers who install solar (Chapter 5). The key to presenting the right solution to your customer is not only knowing *which* of these benefits are applicable and matter the most to your customer, but also knowing *how* to present them. Some financial details only apply to certain customers, such as the *payback period*, or the *rate of return* of a cash investment, while others are relevant across-the-board, such as the *avoided cost of power.*

The details of financial benefits are often depicted in different ways on a solar proposal. For example, a simple graph showing the ever-increasing expense of electricity without solar, compared to the lower and more steady cost of electricity for solar customers:

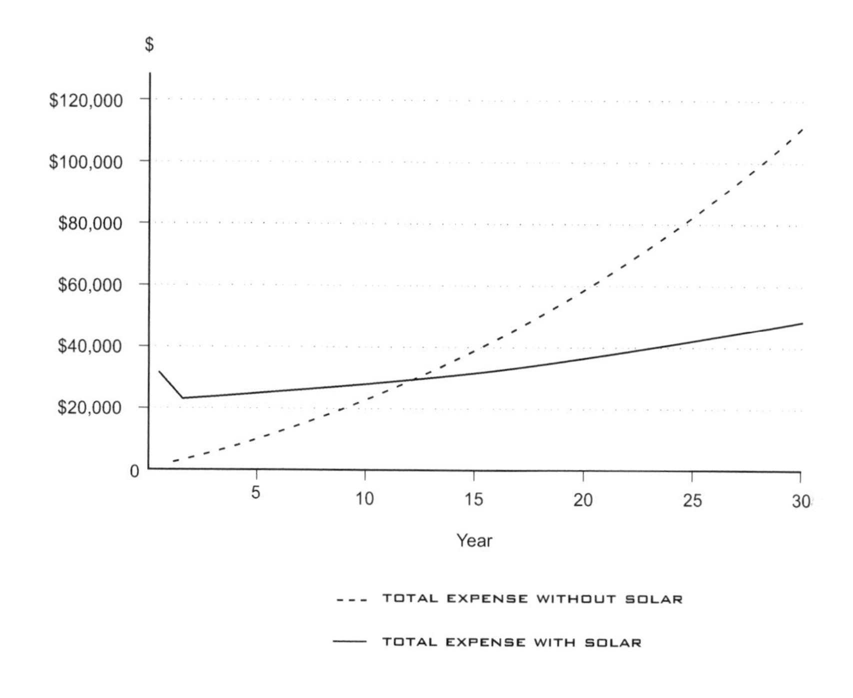

Fig.21. Amount of Money Spent on Electricity

Another common item in solar proposals is the cash-flow table that details the total costs and savings for customers, including the payments and credits they will receive over time—also showing their break-even point. This example shows a cash-paying customer with a payback of thirteen years:

Year	Utility Bill (Without Solar)	New Utility Bill	Solar Payment	Federal Tax Credit	Net Savings	Cumulative Savings & Earnings
0	$ -	$ -	$ 30,907	$ -	$ (30,907)	$ (30,907)
1	$ 2,408	$ 72	$ -	$ 9,272	$ 11,608	$ (19,299)
2	$ 2,485	$ 15	$ -	$ -	$ 2,470	$ (16,829)
3	$ 2,565	$ 27	$ -	$ -	$ 2,538	$ (14,291)
4	$ 2,648	$ 40	$ -	$ -	$ 2,608	$ (11,683)
5	$ 2,734	$ 55	$ -	$ -	$ 2,679	$ (9,004)
...	...	...	...	...	...	...
10	$ 3,220	$ 138	$ -	$ -	$ 3,082	$ (5,743)
15	$ 3,812	$ 256	$ -	$ -	$ 3,556	$ 6,182
20	$ 4,532	$ 401	$ -	$ -	$ 4,131	$ 20,458
25	$ 5,408	$ 588	$ -	$ -	$ 4,820	$ 38,243
30	$ 6,474	$ 830	$ -	$ -	$ 5,644	$ **59,867**

Fig.22. Solar Investment Cash Flow Table

In addition to the graphs showing the rising costs of electricity and cash-flow tables that detail payments, savings, and earnings, solar proposals often include a table with a line-by-line summary of the customer's investment and the financial benefits they can expect to enjoy:

Simple Payback Year:		13
20-Year Internal Rate of Return (Pre-Tax):	$	9.4%
20-Year Electricity Savings:	$	43,929
Total 20-Year Net Savings & Earnings:	$	20,458
Total 25-Year Net Savigns & Earnings:	$	38,243
Average Increase in Home Value (Day One):	$	21,315

Fig.23. Solar Investment Summary

These different displays of the financial benefits allow you to identify the best way of presenting this information. Paying attention to how your customers respond to different kinds of data helps you focus on the right details and guides you when comparing financing options or comparing your quote to the competition. A detailed review of your customer's investment—loan payments, federal tax credits and other incentives, and calculating an increase in the value of their home—should focus on their specific situations and the details that they have expressed interest in—*"I think I have answered all of your questions so far. Is there anything that is still unclear?"*

PREPARING TO CLOSE THE CUSTOMER: GOAL REVIEW AND HANDLING OBJECTIONS

As you finish presenting the benefits to your customer, the last step of the solution is to refer back to your customer's goals list to check off everything you have covered so far. If any questions remain, take this time to answer them. At this point, you are ready to make your first step toward closing the sale, which we call a *soft close*. Now that you have presented solar as a solution to your customer's problems, a means of achieving their goals, and described the benefits of the solar PV system you recommend, you will find out if you have done enough—*"Do you have everything you need to make a decision?"* Other examples of a soft close include, *"Is there anything you feel is missing from the solution I am recommending?"* or *"Is something holding you back from moving forward today?"*

Give your customer time to answer, and as any additional questions, concerns, or objections come up, keep writing them down on the goals list. You should feel confident that you have prepared for this moment by creating a solution with your customer in mind, and it's okay to remind your customer of this—"*This solution meets all of the goals we came up with together. Is there anything else you need to get started on your solar project?*"

By now, your customer has likely come to a decision in their mind, and your job is to make it as easy as possible to move ahead with their investment. Your customer may be ready to go, and if that is the case, you can dive right into the contract and get your customer's project in the queue. If not, the last part of the Solar Sales Method will help you navigate the final steps to winning your customer's business.

One final note before we move onto the close: if you have reached this point and either you or your customer still have serious doubts that solar is a worthwhile investment, you can still acknowledge that what you are selling is not a good fit. It's okay to admit to your customer that solar is not a good choice for them, which not only demonstrates your integrity but saves both of you the time and energy of chasing something that will not work in the end.

CHECKLIST FOR THE PERFECT SOLUTION

✓ Arrive with a proposal prepared but plan on taking a few moments *before* presenting the solution to revise your proposal to meet the customer's goals and preferences that you have discovered during your sales meeting.

✓ Build in a few points during the sales meeting to stop and confirm that your customer understands what you are showing them—*"Does this make sense to you?"* Ask for feedback about specific aspects of the proposal—*"What do you think about this so far?"* And make sure they don't have additional questions—*"Are there any other questions coming up for you?"*

✓ Do not discuss pricing or offer ballpark estimates until you are sure that your customer is convinced that the benefits of solar will outweigh the costs.

✓ Take a few minutes to discuss *how* the price of your customer's project is calculated, especially in competitive situations and with "adders" that increase the cost of your customer's project. Make sure your customer knows how to compare prices and that you are there to help. Competitors may omit an adder until the customer has signed the contract, so make it clear that the price you are showing them is unlikely to change after they sign up.

✓ Do not move onto the close until you have shown the customer how you can achieve each of the items on their goals list and answered every question they have asked until this point.

CHAPTER 12

STEP 5 - THE CLOSE: MAKING A DEAL

Most of the pressure of the sales process falls on closing a sale—when the prospect becomes the customer. Sales professionals in every industry are ranked by their close ratios, performance reviews focus on how many sales are made, and success is generally determined by how much business a salesperson generates. Of course, without the close, there can be no sale, but in reality, the final step in the Solar Sales Method carries the least weight if the previous four steps have been executed properly.

As you begin the final step of the Solar Sales Method, *the close*, you are approaching the "moment of truth." More accurately, this is when you will find out if you've understood your customer's goals and effectively met their needs—if you have identified a problem and proposed an appealing solution. Although this is the last step, try to avoid thinking of this as the *end* of the sales process. Instead, consider it the *beginning* of the customer's journey going solar.

The primary goal of the close is to make a *deal* with your customer. The close is your opportunity to ask the customer for their business—to agree on a deal that lives up to your customer's expectations. More importantly, come to an agreement that both you and your company can follow through on.

Even if you have gone through each step of the Solar Sales Method and demonstrated that the solution is the customer's best choice, they may still have reservations. Whatever is holding them back may not be a logical decision but an emotional one. In these cases, repeating facts and figures or bringing up the benefits repeatedly will not be enough to break down the remaining barriers for your customers.

In each of the following sections, you will learn some methods and strategies to demonstrate solutions, explain advantages and benefits, and overcome any remaining objections. You have brought your customer to the end of the hallway, closing each door along the way. Now, you are at the decision-making point, and it is time to walk them through the final doorway.

ASKING FOR THE BUSINESS

After all of the effort you have put in to bring the sales process to a close, the simplest and most important thing you can do is *ask* your customer for their business. It may seem obvious to *you* that you have reached the decision-making point, but this is not always evident to your customers. You have worked hard to get to this point. Now, it is time to make it as easy as possible for your prospect to become your customer. This can be accomplished by asking a simple question—*"Are you ready to move forward today?"*

Asking your customer to sign up is the natural next step in the sales process. You have shown them that you are focused on meeting their needs, you have identified solar as a means to achieve their goals, and you should have already helped your customer choose the solution that they are most interested in. If you've accomplished these three things, there is a high probability your customer has already decided to go solar in their head. Now, it's time to get them to act on it—and choose to work with you.

Remember that your customer is making a decision that will affect them for many years. The sales cycle may be nearing its end, but their solar project will last for decades to come. When asking for your customer's business, provide them with space and time to respond, waiting quietly for their answer. In moments of silence, it can be tempting to start talking and to reach back into your list of "reasons why they should go solar," but waiting for their answer shows that you're interested in what they think and not just selling your product.

Finally, when asking for the business, it is important to be clear and direct—*"Can I get you signed up today?"* or *"Are you ready to get started on the paperwork?"* Avoiding vague and open questions such as, *"What do you think?"* or *"How does it look?"* They're less likely to lead to a decision. Straightforward questions and a direct call-to-action ensures you will never lose a customer because you didn't ask.

This doesn't mean that asking your customer to work with you will always elicit a decision. Sometimes, it takes a few tries to bring your customer to a decision, which is why it's important to focus on the closing steps in a sale and remember that you may not always close the customer during your first meeting. Nevertheless, if your customer is not ready to commit at the outset of *the close*, the following strategies can help bring hesitant customers to agree to a deal.

CREATING A SENSE OF URGENCY

One of the most common closing strategies in sales is created by a *sense of urgency* that encourages the customer to make a decision before it's too late. Examples of the *urgency close* include "weekend only" sales or "only one left in stock" statements, which are designed to give the customer the impression that their opportunity will be gone if they hesitate. The urgency close appears in many forms in the solar industry because rebates, incentives, and tax credits all have expiration dates, solar proposals and price quotes are only valid for a period of time, and in general, creating a sense of urgency is a common method for closing undecided customers.

The sense of urgency is practically built into the solar industry—rebates and incentives only last so long, and the Federal ITC is yet again slated to expire at the end of 2021. Currently, a sense of urgency exists naturally for customers who understand that a 22 percent federal tax credit can significantly improve the financial benefits of their investment. Creating a sense of urgency for customers is as simple as pointing out that the longer they wait, the less likely they are to qualify for the incentives currently available.

A sense of urgency is not only created by explaining what the customer has to lose, but also by establishing an emotional connection between the customer and their decision to go solar—*"How important is qualifying for the federal tax credit?"* Posing this question encourages the customer to really consider what they will miss out on if they wait too long to make a decision.

Creating urgency for customers is a delicate process and works best when it is intended to help a customer make the best choice, *not* as a method for pressuring a customer to go solar. When you are honest with your customer and presenting them with reasons time is of the essence, they will be more likely to bring themselves to a decision than if you are simply putting pressure on them. Some examples of creating urgency in the solar sales process include:

1. **Getting on the installation schedule (for tax credit):** *"The sooner you are in the installation queue, the greater the chance you'll qualify for the tax credit before the end of the year. Do you need more information to make a decision?"*

2. **Getting on the installation schedule (for production):** *"You'll be on the schedule and installed by the summer when production is highest. Is there anything else you need to see to move forward?"*

3. **Pricing expiration:** *"This quote is valid for the next two weeks, but after that, I'll have to re-run the numbers. Does that give you enough time to make a decision?"*

4. **End-of-the-Month (or Quarter, or Year) Promotion:** *"I can offer you a $500 discount if you sign up by the end of the month. Do you have everything you need to decide by then?"*

The urgency close has its time and place, and while it may help some customers to make a decision, it may leave others with a bad taste in their mouth. Signing up the customer at the end of your first sales meeting—a *one-call-close*—ultimately saves you time and effort that would otherwise be spent on follow-up meetings, contract signings, and responding to additional questions, concerns, and objections. Creating a sense of urgency is intended to encourage your customer to decide sooner and understand that time is of the essence but be careful not to use it as an ultimatum or simply a means of shortening the sales cycle to save you from doing more work.

If your customer is unwilling to make a decision at the end of the consultation, it is better to understand *why* than to push harder. Find out what is holding your customer back—*"Is there something else you need to make a decision today?"* or *"Is there something preventing you from making a decision today?"* You can then come up with the best strategy for what comes next.

Whatever the customer's hesitation—be it because they want to get a least three quotes, they need to talk it over with their accountant, or they are unsure of the savings—it can either expose something you've missed or help you understand what the customer needs to take the final steps with you. This will bring you to another important aspect of the close, explaining what comes next on the path to going solar.

THE NEXT STEPS

The close is not complete until your customer's signature is on the contract, and no sooner. In fact, the close is often the longest part of the sales cycle. It may last a few months if that's how long it takes for your customer to come to a decision. Because of this, you must prepare your customer for what comes next. *The next steps* in the process of going solar include everything from contract signing to installation and all points in between.

On average, it takes three months from the time a customer signs a contract until their solar PV system is up and running. The reason for this is because several installation steps can't be rushed—such as applying for permits with local authorities, building inspections, and getting a net meter installed by the utility—even though it only takes a day or two to complete the actual installation on the customer's home. Discussing the next steps not only sets expectations for your customer, but it also presents another opportunity to bring them to a decision-making point. Discussing the next steps is a closing technique. The next steps are made up of the following series of events:

1. **Review and Sign the Agreement:** The contract signing is a call-to-action that sets all of the next steps in motion. To begin, look over the agreement with your customer to give you a chance to review the details of their contract so they can feel comfortable with what they are signing up for. Reviewing the agreement ranges from confirming warranties and the customer's responsibilities to explaining production guarantees and other details that the customer has asked specific questions about. The goal of reviewing the

agreement is to make your customer feel comfortable making the decision to move forward. After the contract has been signed, your *project manager* will take over to coordinate the next steps leading up to the installation.

2. **Site Survey:** Once the contract is signed, the process of going solar officially begins. The first step following a signed contract is the *site survey,* which is completed by a technician who visits the customer's home. During the site survey, the technician takes pictures and measurements of the customer's roof, verifies the structural integrity of the home, the electrical capacity of the distribution panel, and records *solar access* data to confirm that the system you have recommended will perform as expected. The site survey generally occurs a week or two after the contract signing, depending on how busy your company is and when a site technician is available to complete this step.

3. **Engineering and Finalizing Design:** When the details of your customer's home are confirmed, the project manager enlists engineers to complete the *final design, one-line diagrams,* and *structural engineering review.* These steps are necessary to ensure that the customer's PV system meets local building codes, and you have the design documents required for permitting and inspections. In addition, if there are any changes to the system you presented to your customer, a *change order* is created, and the adjustments must be presented to the customer, who will need to sign off

on the final design.* The process of engineering and finalizing designs generally takes place within a few weeks of the site visit. However, this also depends on your company's resources and bandwidth of the engineering team.

4. **Permitting and Utility Application:** When the final design is complete and approved, the project management team takes the next step to submit the diagrams and documents for permitting and utility interconnection approval. This step is taken on behalf of the customer, and it's often the longest in the post-sale process because it depends entirely on the utility company and local permitting offices.

5. **Material Procurement:** As the project manager waits for permitting approval, they prepare a bill of materials to procure the equipment needed to complete the installation. Once the materials have been acquired, they are "staged" and prepared for the installation team. This step typically takes place a week or two before the scheduled installation.

6. **System Installation:** Once your customer's permits are approved and their equipment is procured and staged, their project is put on the installation schedule. The project manager confirms the dates with the customer, and when the time comes, the installation team arrives to complete the construction. On average, it takes a little less than three

* For example, if you presented a twenty-one-panel system but the engineers find that only twenty panels will fit, a change order is created that shows the revised design, price, and savings. Ultimately, you will be responsible for returning to thecustomer with any changes, which is why it is best to be conservative with your designs and production estimates.

months from contract signing to get to this point, but the actual installation only takes a couple of days.

7. **Inspection:** Following the installation, the next step is to wait for the local authority to inspect and approve the system to ensure that it is safe and operable. This may require access to the customer's home, and in these cases, it must be scheduled with the homeowner. Once the system is installed, the inspection will likely occur within a week or two, but this depends on the local inspection office.

8. **Interconnection:** When a solar PV system is approved by the local building authorities, there is one final step before the system is ready to be turned on: installing the *net meter.* The customer's utility company is alerted that the PV system is approved and is awaiting its net meter. The customer doesn't need to be present to install the net meter, which should take place within a few weeks of the utility being informed that the PV system passed inspection.

9. **System Powered On:** Once the net meter is installed, the customer's PV system is ready to be turned on. The master disconnect switch is flipped on, and your customer is officially producing their own electricity! For this final step, it is best to schedule a time to go to your customer's home to physically turn the system on with them and walk them through the system components and monitoring systems.

As you explain the steps above to your customer, you are preparing them for the process of going solar, building excitement for what is to come. Furthermore, reviewing this process provides an opportunity to prepare the customer to make a decision if they haven't committed to going solar by this point. In this case, explaining the next steps sets you up to ask your customers for their business *again*.

Clearly and directly asking your customers to work with you ensures you won't miss the opportunity to make a sale, but until you have gotten a verbal commitment, you will need to inquire again. Asking for your customer's business two or three times is not uncommon, and it can mean the difference between signing up a new customer or walking away from a potential sale.

CLOSING TECHNIQUES

The close is the fifth and final step of the Solar Sales Method, and while every step is critical to the overall process of selling solar, there is no sale without a successful close—although one could argue that without completing the other steps, there is no sale either. Like each of the previous steps, certain tricks and techniques will help you become more effective in closing customers. Through practice and experience, you can improve your sales effectiveness by employing the following closing techniques to bring your customer across the finish line.

1. **Direct Close:** Ask for the sale and wait for the customer to respond. Asking directly—"*Are you ready to move forward?*"—is the simplest and most straightforward approach to closing customers. Wait for your customer to respond and give them time to think the decision through. The more time you give them, the more thoughtful their answer will be, whether they agree or explain why they're not ready.

2. **Assumptive Close:** Skip to the conclusion that you are going to close the customer. Throughout the sales process, you are collecting "yesses" from your customer. For example, *"Yes, I understand that solar can save me a lot of money,"* or *"Yes, I see why this is better than paying my utility bill."* Each "yes" brings them closer to their decision to go solar. In situations where no barriers remain, you can make the assumption that your customer is ready to sign up and simply bring them to the next step—*"So, let's get your project started!"*

3. **Option Close:** Present the customer with a choice to move forward with. As much as you try to provide your customer with *one* option, you will inevitably find yourself comparing different financing options—and sometimes different system sizes—with a customer. At some point, there is no longer the question of "if" but rather, "which one." This decision-making point creates the opportunity for the customer to make their choice—*"You have two great options here. Which one would you like to move forward with?"* Once they choose which option they prefer, they will be primed to make the next decision to move forward with you.

4. **Summary Close:** Review your recommendation and reiterate the benefits. Perhaps the most instinctive closing technique is the summary close, which is a final review of the many reasons your customer has expressed interest in solar—their key motivators, the problems they are experiencing, and the goals they wish to achieve. In other words, it involves asking the customer, *"Why not?"* or coming up with an explanation of what is holding them back. If asking your customer what

is preventing them from moving forward does not result in a sale, at the very least, you will find out their remaining questions, concerns, or objections to address.

5. **Special Opportunity Close**: Provide some incentive to your customer that will help them make a timely decision. Customers unable or unwilling to make a decision (the "tire-kickers" and the "fence-sitters") can take up valuable time over weeks and months of follow-up as you check in to ask, *"Are you ready to make a decision?"* The special opportunity close provides some extra incentive to customers without the need for strong persuasion or manipulative techniques. Examples include pricing discounts, equipment upgrades, additional referral bonuses, or even gift cards to a restaurant or store of their choosing. These opportunities may last for a week, until the end of the month, or however long you can allow your customer to make their decision—*"If it will help you make a decision, I can offer you a $500 discount if you sign up by the end of the month."* The special opportunity close is often a last-ditch effort to wrap up the sales process with one customer so that you can focus your energy on others.

6. **The Anti-Close**: Selling with integrity is not just an idea, but a practice that begins from the very first interaction you have with a customer and lasts until the very end. The anti-close—which will likely occur after the third or even fourth time you ask for the business—is intended to create a sense of closure for both you and your customer—*"This solution*

meets all of the goals we have discussed together, but if you're still not convinced, then perhaps solar is not right for you." On the one hand, it gives your customer the chance to say "no." On the other hand, it gives *you* the chance to walk away from a customer who simply isn't a good candidate for solar or might end up wasting your time. Your willingness to leave the ball in their court is not manipulative but evidence of your integrity. If the customer ends up changing their mind, chances are they will call you—the consultant who gracefully walked away—instead of the pushy salesperson who wouldn't let it rest.

This list of closing techniques is by no means exhaustive, and there are hundreds of ways to close a deal with customers. The close may be the final step in the Solar Sales Method—and a necessary one—but this does not make it the most *important* step. As you grow in your sales career, you will have many opportunities to learn new skills, adopt new strategies, and adjust your sales process to many different customers with various personalities, beliefs, and goals. Similarly, your ability to adapt to different kinds of people will help you navigate the ever-changing technologies, financing options, and benefits of going solar. Through all of the changes in the future, the Solar Sales Method that you have learned to apply is the foundation that remains intact.

CHECKLIST FOR THE PERFECT CLOSE

- ✓ Check-in with your own process so you can stay on track: make sure you have executed each step of the Solar Sales Method, stuck with the agenda you set at the beginning, and maintained focus on the customer's questions, concerns, and goals.
- ✓ Before you ask for the business, revisit the goals list with your customer and cross all of the items off the list—visually showing them that you have answered all of their questions and your recommendation will meet all of their goals.
- ✓ Have a plan for the next steps. If your customer doesn't sign up after your first sales meeting, don't fret. This can be accomplished by discussing a follow-up plan with your customer and find out how and when they'd like to hear from you or practice the "Rule of Three."*

* The Rule of Three is a follow-up strategy to keep in touch with customers based on the number three: 1) Send a follow-up email to your customer three hours after your meeting to thank them, recap your conversation and the system you recommend— including a summary of costs and benefits—and the goals they will achieve. Let them know you'll be available for additional questions and will stay in touch. 2) Check in with your customer every three days following your meeting, trying not to let three days go by without some kind of communication to or from your customer—email, phone calls, or text. This is not only to see if they're ready to sign up but also to answer any remaining questions or provide additional content such as newsletters or customer testimonials. 3) Continue this process for three weeks following your sales meeting. Once you have reached this point, if you haven't established a follow-up plan with your customer, it's a good time for the Anti-close. By now, you've spent enough time on the customer to feel comfortable moving on to other more responsive customers.

- ✓ Keep practicing! Like all unfamiliar things, applying the Solar Sales Method may feel clunky and unnatural at first, and simply reading this book will not make you a more effective salesperson. There is no substitute for experience, execution, and putting the lessons you have learned into action over and over again.

PART 4

PUTTING IT ALL INTO ACTION

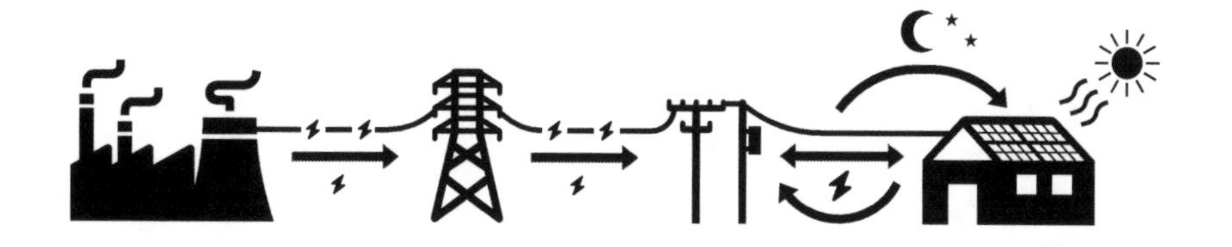

CHAPTER 13

BECOMING A NATURAL SALES PROFESSIONAL

At some point in your life, you probably met someone who made you feel comfortable right away. For some unknown reason, when they spoke about something, it just made sense to you, and if they recommended something, you just had to have it. While it's possible to have a knack for connecting with people, the truth is that "natural" salespeople don't possess some superpower to make you want to buy something—they're simply interested in *helping you.*

Selling doesn't come naturally to everybody. Even the best salespeople are constantly learning new lessons and finding new ways to approach and help their customers. Whether selling something is "easy" or a product "sells itself," the transaction follows a sales process that establishes a relationship between the buyer and the seller—the customer and the product. With practice, you can learn to build deeper relationships with your customer and create stronger bonds with the product you are selling. So, how do you develop these skills?

In Part 4, you will learn how to develop your own personal style and strengthen your sales skills in order to become a "natural" sales professional to carry you toward better performance. We will explore opportunities for deepening relationships with customers, learning when to push forward and when to pull back, and other tricks for strengthening the most important skills for closing sales.

FINDING YOUR OWN STYLE

Sales professionals do not reach their peak performance if they're pretending to be somebody they are not. Becoming a great salesperson doesn't happen overnight—or by the time you finish this book—but takes time and commitment. Just like the Solar Sales Method that follows a series of steps that can't be rushed or skipped over, finding your own "natural" style requires practice and determination.

1. **Act Natural:** Be yourself and you'll never have to put on an act. As you approach your customers, remember that you're not there to perform or to persuade but to help your customer see solar as a worthwhile investment that will improve their quality of life and provide many benefits. Trying to be someone or something you are not is one way to lose your customer's trust or come off as unauthentic.

2. **Take Your Time:** Experience can't be rushed, and you won't become a top performer by simply reading a book. Developing effective sales skills takes practice, which comes with time and experience. Create a plan for your sales process that you can stick with. That way, each time you meet a new customer, you will continue developing good habits. It may take time, but eventually, it will become natural.

3. **Keep Learning as You Go:** There will always be more to learn and new ways to grow. The solar industry is constantly changing, so you will continue to learn about new prices, policies, and products. In addition to adapting to the changing landscape, one thing top performers have in common is they continue seeking out ways to improve their knowledge and skills by watching and learning from others around them. You may develop your own style and structure, but it's never too late to learn something new.

LEARNING TO LISTEN

By the time you finish this book and complete your new-hire training, you're going to know a lot about solar. You will be bursting with knowledge and information, and you'll probably want to tell your customers *everything* you know about solar. Though it may seem like a good idea to teach your customers as much as you know, it's important to resist this urge. *Slow down* and remember that being effective in sales revolves around *listening* to your customer.

After learning the Solar Sales Method, you've probably figured out that selling solar depends more on your knowledge of your customer than how much you know about solar. Your goal is to present a solar

PV system to your customer—one that meets all of their expectations and brings them plenty of benefits—by making sure the system they sign up for is right for them. From the very first conversation you have with a customer, this is made possible by listening. Here are summaries of the steps that we've covered so far, and some new tricks that you can use to develop your listening skills during the sales process:

1. **Start with a clean sheet of paper or a "Customer Account Worksheet."** Have a notepad or create a new worksheet at the beginning of the sales process to take notes during conversations. You will learn a lot about your customer from your first introductory call to the day of your contract signing. While customer relationship management (CRM) software will help you keep track of interactions with your customers, your notepad will be more conducive to taking quick notes during your conversations with customers.

2. **Find out what questions they want answered.** Write down any questions your customer asks on your worksheet or on the "goals list" you create with your customers. Begin each conversation with, *"What questions do you have for me today?"* and write out each question so by the end of your conversation, you can physically cross off each question that you have answered. If you are unable to answer any questions during your conversation, return to this sheet before calling your customer back so you can be sure to address their question the next time you speak.

3. **Pay attention to how much you're talking.** You may find yourself wishing your customer would talk more at times, but chances are your customer never really wants to hear you go on and on about solar. Each step of the Solar Sales Method suggests a balance between talking and listening: The customer should do 80 percent of the talking during the interview and the validation. You should do 80 percent of the talking during the presentation and the solution. During the close, try to keep it around 50 percent each. Of course, learning to listen doesn't just mean being quiet. Sometimes your customer will need you to tell them more. As a rule, let your customer talk as much as they'd like and only go into deeper detail on a subject when your customer asks for it. When there are no more questions, it's a good sign that you can move on to the next step, whatever it may be.

4. **Less is more.** There are times when the amount of information and detail about going solar can seem overwhelming—especially for customers who are starting from a clean slate. After going over the many facts and figures, prices and production estimates, payback periods and savings charts, sometimes it helps take a break, step back, and let it all sink in. This might mean giving the customer a day or two, which would require you to create a follow-up plan with them. Another way to slow things down is to suggest a site walk and have the customer show you their electric panel and the location of their utility meter. Or, you can always step outside to call your manager while you give them some time to think things over and discuss with their partner.

The more you practice these actions, the more you will find that being born with "natural" sales skills has little to do with your professional success. Becoming a high-performance sales professional takes time and effort, but your goal is not to change who you are. Rather, becoming a natural salesperson means becoming more of *yourself* by leveraging your unique abilities, taking advantage of your talents and passions, understanding what drives you, and cementing these skills in your toolbox to help your customers go solar.

CRAFTING SALES INTEGRITY

Crafting a career as a high-integrity sales professional is a choice. You have already chosen to pursue a career in the solar industry, and you will continue to make important choices every day as you help homeowners go solar. High-performance careers driven by integrity are guided by a commitment to yourself, your customers, and the following principles:

Start out on the right foot. As you read this book, some lessons will resonate with you, your style, and your personality, while others seem like a chore or they don't quite fit your approach. Whether you follow 10 percent or 90 percent of the advice and methods in this book, you are in complete control of your future as a solar sales professional. As you begin your career—or take the next step on your path—it is essential to build the right foundation.

This means choosing whether to make your name as a high-pressure and manipulative sales professional, or a customer-focused and honest consultant. Your reputation is often determined by the choices you make early in your career, but it's never too late to redefine yourself. The Solar Sales Method is designed to help you make the right choices in the early days of your career to craft a reputation of honesty and integrity. By defining yourself and your career this way, you will find your customers are much more likely to recommend you to friends and family, your colleagues will be more willing to send leads your way, and the efficacy of your sales will increase.

Most of the choices you will make as a sales professional are within your control. Will you approach the customer with conservative solar solutions or push the limits? Will you focus on the customer's needs or base your sales pitches on what you think is best? Will you try to convince customers to go solar or help them make a considered decision? Regardless, one major decision will affect your career more than any other: what company will you work for?

Choose the right company. There are many different roles in the solar industry (Chapter 4), and putting yourself in a position to maximize your skills and abilities is vital for your success. In addition, there are also many different companies, and it is as important, if not critical, to choose the right company to work for, one with values that align with yours and rewards your ambitions.

Most corporate solar companies in the United States have clearly defined *mission statements*, *visions*, and *values*—cultural guidelines that you can familiarize yourself with before applying or accepting a position. There are a few ways to learn what your experience will be working for a company and what will be expected of you. Ensure you are making the right decision by employing the following strategies:

1. **Go on a "ride-along."** Before accepting a position, attend a sales meeting with one of the organization's consultants. You can tell a lot about the culture of a company if your future colleagues are insistent, manipulative, and stressed out about their performance. These are all telltale signs that the company prioritizes sales and performance over quality and integrity.

2. **Review their new-hire training process.** Ask to see an outline of the new-hire training process. Look for a comprehensive curriculum that includes *skill development* topics in addition to solar 101 and how to use the company's proposal tools and CRM. If the company has a long-term training strategy, that is a good sign you're on the right track. A company that doesn't have something to show or unwilling to share its training methods is more likely unorganized or doesn't have a well-developed training program.

3. **Get third-party verification.** The truth is that it's pretty easy to fabricate positive reviews online and cover up bad sales or installation practices. You can dig a little deeper by asking to speak with other employees in the organization (not just the ones interested in hiring you) or even talk to existing customers. If that isn't available to you, try checking other sources, such as the Better Business Bureau for complaints against the business, or Glassdoor to find out what previous employees have to say about their experience.

Working for the right company—one that resonates with your personal values—is one of the greatest advantages you can have as a sales professional. If you find yourself working for a business that disregards what you find most important, it can start to show in your performance. It is difficult to sell with confidence if you don't believe your company will live up to the expectations you are setting with your customer.

Setting Expectations and Following Through. From the very first interaction you have with your customer, they will begin developing expectations for the company and the product you are selling. Lead generators prepare customers for what they will encounter during a solar sales consultation, but a new set of expectations begins forming as soon as you begin talks with a new customer.

Selling with integrity is a process that begins with the first interaction and ends when the customer has received all that they have expected. In other words, selling with integrity means *following through* on what you have promised.

In the big picture, you have a relatively small role to play in a customer going solar. Once the contract is signed, the bulk of the work occurs during the steps of engineering, procurement, and construction (EPC), which end with your customer's solar PV system producing electricity for years to come. Despite your limited involvement, you will remain the face of those expectations, and every delay or mistake that may happen will fall onto your shoulders.

This is yet another reason why choosing the right company is so important. You and your customer both need to believe that their solar panels will be installed on the timeline you've laid out, that they will be installed in the same location that you have presented, and that the installers will take care of their property just as you assured. To put it simply: your word is only as good as the company you represent.

Setting the right expectations for your customer is just the beginning. The follow-through is where it matters most. Letting your customer know what will happen from the get-go is essential for starting a customer relationship off on the right foot and maintaining it over time. The more time you spend explaining to unhappy customers why something didn't happen, the less time you'll have to focus on signing up new customers. More importantly, if your company follows through on its promises, your customers will be more likely to have a good experience and bring you more business by referring their family, friends, and neighbors.

Selling with Confidence. Each of the last few sections—starting on the right foot, choosing the right company, and following through on your word—have a direct impact on your confidence as a sales professional. The common definition of *integrity* is being honest and having strong moral principles. However, the second definition of *integrity* also resonates here: "The state of being whole and undivided."

Crafting your reputation as an honest and thoughtful salesperson with strong moral principles is a personal choice; however, if you don't work for a company that prioritizes these same standards, your confidence is likely to suffer. If you are uncertain of the promises you make, unsure about the colleagues who represent you, and find yourself struggling to keep those promises with your customers, you are likely to become uncertain about your ability to sell.

When your sales practices are aligned with your company's values, you are much more likely to find yourself feeling "whole." If you believe that your company will live up to the expectations that you set for your customers, you are much more likely to find yourself feeling "undivided." Integrity begins with you and extends to your company. By focusing on these values, you can build confidence in yourself and the product you represent.

As you follow your career in sales, you will encounter many challenges and bumps in the road. Whether they are personal or related to your company, do not dwell on these challenges as setbacks but instead treat them as opportunities for growth. The solar industry as a whole is not without flaws and uncertainty, and you will inevitably encounter delays, mistakes, and unfulfilled promises no matter which company you work for.

The more experience you have selling solar, the more natural the sales process will become. As you put the Solar Sales Method into practice, it will eventually require less effort as helping your customer before all else becomes an instinct. The more time you spend at your company, the more you will come to understand how things work, which will give you the confidence to set the right expectations with your customers and to overcome any hiccups, deal with challenges head-on, and come out the other side as strong as you went in.

Becoming a "natural" is not about being born with some special ability to sell. It's about committing yourself to be your best. As you find your own style, learn to listen to customers, and craft a reputation of honesty and integrity, you will continue developing your sales skills.

CHAPTER 14

HOW TO DEVELOP YOUR SALES SKILLS AND INCREASE YOUR SALES VOLUME

Throughout this book, the term "customer" is used as a general expression to describe the people you will work with throughout your sales career. One reason for this is because whether you are speaking to a prospective customer or a client who already signed a contract, they should both be treated with the same attentiveness and respect. In addition, the process of generating *sales leads*—potential clients who express interest in your product—

shares many similarities to selling. Developing sales skills doesn't only happen during the selling process.

Generating a lead is truly the first step towards a sale—and arguably the most important because without the lead, there is nobody to sell to. As a solar sales professional, lead generation is an unparalleled method for developing selling skills *and* increasing your sales volume. While solar companies can employ many forms of lead generation to create business, including digital advertising, cold-calling, and direct-mail flyers, none are as effective as actively engaging in lead-generating activities yourself.

The solar industry is continually evolving, but one aspect of sales origination remains constant—the success of door-to-door lead generation, or *canvassing*. What makes canvassing such an important part of the solar industry?

To answer this question, you first need to understand that canvassing isn't just a fancy word for door-to-door sales. Canvassing does not typically entail a transaction or the direct sale of a product or service. Historically, door-to-door sales was a popular approach for adept salesmen and companies selling household products and services such as knives, vacuums, water filters, or satellite TV. One thing all of these products have in common is the point-of-sale takes place on the doorstep. In comparison, canvassing for residential solar is intended to qualify customers, provide information, and stimulate interest with the primary goal of scheduling a solar consultation that takes place at a later date.

For solar sales professionals, canvassing is important for many reasons: first, it is a marketing strategy—not a sales strategy—that provides the opportunity for more direct and effective interactions with potential customers. Second, sales consultants who engage in canvassing activities and make first contact with their customers have more control over the overall sales process. Third, the experience of going door-to-door provides an invaluable opportunity to practice engaging with customers and developing sales skills that are applicable later on in the sales process.

Yet another important reason canvassing is so effective for selling solar is because going door-to-door is the most direct and effective way to qualify customers. Direct, because this strategy results in a face-to-face conversation with potential customers more often. Effective, because solar power is not a one-size-fits-all product and standing on the doorstep of a home is the best way to determine if it's a viable option.

Roughly one-quarter of the homes in the United States qualify for solar, depending on various factors that include the direction that a roof is facing, whether there is enough roof space, and if major shading concerns exist. A well-trained solar professional standing on the sidewalk in front of a house can quickly determine whether solar would be a good investment for the homeowner. Unlike direct-mail flyers or digital advertising, the ability to pre-qualify a home before attempting to talk to the owner saves valuable time and money and frees up the canvasser to focus on the most qualified customers.

Traditional marketing campaigns are more expensive and less ineffective, especially for a product as complicated and nuanced as solar power. For example, the average response rate to a direct mail campaign is around 2 percent. That means a solar company that sends out 10,000 flyers might generate roughly 200 responses. Since only a quarter of homes in the U.S. are fit for solar, only 50 of those who respond are likely to qualify. The other 150 responses end up wasting company time and resources, only to be disappointed that they're not qualified to go solar. Ultimately, direct mail campaigns have a higher likelihood of resulting in unhappy non-customers who are upset that they have been misled or are simply frustrated by receiving more junk mail.

Compared to traditional marketing campaigns, canvassing is more effective, and it lowers the *cost per acquisition*—how much a company spends on acquiring a customer. A small team of well-trained canvassers can generate fifty well-qualified leads in a few days. Canvassing provides an opportunity to speak directly to would-be decision-makers, and such face-to-face interactions result in more informative conversations than any other marketing approach.

Canvassing is one of the most efficient forms of marketing in the residential solar industry and typically results in one of the highest close ratios of any marketing strategy—usually only second to referrals. It is a cost-effective way to generate new sales leads, but it is also an effective way to develop your sales skills while growing your *sales pipeline*—the number of prospective clients you are working with. Consider the following reasons canvassing is your shortest path to improving your sales skills and growing your business:

1. Build Stronger Relationships. The ability to provide a positive customer experience—and having complete control over the sales process—from the very beginning is one reason canvassing is so appealing to residential solar companies. Customers who install solar because a canvasser knocked on their door are often impressed by the personalization and connection created between them and their installer in such a short interaction.

The personal touch that canvassing provides is a unique experience that is more memorable than any other marketing approach. Homeowners are much more likely to recall the conversation they had with a canvasser on their doorstep, which leaves a stronger impression than a flyer ever could. Furthermore, meeting somebody in person at their home is more likely to lead to a meaningful discussion about solar. Such personal connections that customers experience from the very beginning of the sales process are more likely to influence the decision they make.

2. Develop Skills and Good Habits. The skills you will develop when canvassing—or engaging in any lead-generating activity—are vital for your success as a sales professional. You don't have to be an extrovert or an expert on solar energy to provide customers with a detailed and informative presentation about how they can benefit from solar—you need practice. Being prepared, knowing how to impart your knowledge clearly, and having practice presenting sales materials are better indicators of success than simply being talkative or educated. Each of these skills is developed while canvassing.

Successful canvassers are diligent and enthusiastic individuals, but the most important quality is the willingness to take on challenges and keep going to the next door despite any obstacles. Going door-to-door presenting solar over and over is a formative practice that develops develop a thick skin and will quickly teach you how to overcome the answer "no"—or at the very least learn how to take rejection in stride. Canvassing is one way to build your sales skills and develop good habits that will go a long way toward a successful sales career.

3. Generate Your Own Business. Whether you work alone, for a small solar company, or a large corporate business, the resources dedicated to lead generation are finite. Canvassing may take more time and energy to generate business, but the financial cost is much lower than advertising, cold calling, and other traditional marketing approaches. Your company may already employ a canvassing team and provide company-generated leads, but what if that's not enough for you?

Many lead-generating businesses sell solar leads today, but paid leads are often under-qualified and over-competitive—unless you pay a premium for exclusive leads. As you sell to more and more customers, you will develop a referral pipeline—generating leads through your existing customers—but this can take some time, and there are limitations. If you want to start generating more business today *and* improve your sales skills, your best option is to incorporate canvassing into your sales strategy.

Taking lead generation into your own hands doesn't mean taking over lead-generation responsibilities for your company or spending all your free time canvassing. However, any time you are in a neighborhood to meet with a customer, you will likely be surrounded by many other homes that are qualified for solar. If you are already in the neighborhood, taking some time to knock on a few doors has virtually no additional costs and can improve your performance. For example, if you have time to kill between appointments, you might use it to knock on a few doors instead of following up with existing clients. Other than the time and energy it takes to walk from house to house, you can make the most of canvassing without sacrificing other responsibilities. Here are three essential strategies to increase your sales volumes:

1. Ask for referrals: At the end of every sales presentation and before you leave your customer's home, you should always ask them for referrals from friends, family, and neighbors. Take it one step further by building some trust and credibility: *"Once your solar panels are installed, and you are pleased with your experience working with me, would you be willing to connect me with three friends, family members, or neighbors who would like to look into solar?"*

2. After every appointment, go knock on at least ten doors in the neighborhood. After *every* appointment—unless you have to rush off to another meeting—give yourself a chance to increase the business potential for each appointment you run: *"I was just meeting with your neighbors about installing solar panels to lower their electric bills and noticed that you also have a great home for solar. Can I show you how solar can save you money, too?"*

Why ten and not just a couple of the immediate neighbors? Canvassing is a numbers game, and if you only knock on two or three doors, you are not only lessening your odds of meeting a prospect but also falling short of getting into the "rhythm" of canvassing. The more homes that can be approached, the greater your chances of starting a conversation with a qualified homeowner—or even finding one at home. What happens if the first door you knock on is a "yes?"

Keep going! There's no limit to how many leads you can generate if you continue, and your confidence and excitement will only serve to increase your chances with the next homeowner. If you show up to a door defeated and cynical, you're starting off on the wrong foot. But if you are beaming from your last success, your chances of another one are much greater. In fact, if you get on a roll, you'll probably want to continue well after the tenth door.

3. Ask your customers for permission—or advice—to approach their neighbors. If you are only going to knock on ten doors after each appointment, wouldn't you want to know who to talk to? Or who *not* to talk to?

At the end of your meeting with a customer, ask them if they have any neighbors who might be interested in talking to you. You should already be in the habit of asking your customers for referrals at the end of every meeting, so this is simply taking it one step further. If your customer hasn't referred you to a family member or friend, maybe they know a neighbor who could benefit from solar.

When you knock on a door that your customer suggested, you will also have an advantage—knowing their name and telling them that somebody sent you. This is especially effective considering other obstacles common to canvassing. For example, over-canvassing neighborhoods causes homeowners to put up "no soliciting" signs or results in neighborhood-wide covenants that prohibit solicitors—or requires expensive permits. If you have a personal connection with a potential homeowner, it is much easier to overcome these barriers.

4. Treat post-appointment canvassing leads as referrals. Referrals are the golden goose of the solar industry—close ratios are higher, cost per acquisition is lower, and when you find a referral "champion," it can generate a windfall of sales. However, the hardest part of developing a referral pipeline is getting the first one. Whether or not your customer tells you which one of their neighbors you should talk to, offering them a referral bonus for any post-appointment canvassing sales you generate is one way to jumpstart a successful referral relationship.

You can explain how your referral program works until you're blue in the face, but words only go so far. Once your customer has a referral check in their hands, it becomes real, and they will probably be much more likely to start looking into their contacts to send more potential customers your way. Your customer may not have referred you to their neighbors, but by showing them that you're interested in helping them earn some extra cash, you are not only stoking their interest in pursuing other referrals but also rewarding them for working with you.

COMMUNITY MARKETING

Canvassing is one way to increase sales volume, regardless of the resources your company puts into generating leads. While canvassing is an effective and affordable way to generate leads in the solar industry, it is not the only way to drum up more business. There are many other opportunities to engage in community-based lead generation, or *field marketing*, either as an individual or as a business.

Aside from canvassing, field marketing strategies include attending local events, developing community alliances, and building partnerships with businesses. All of these strategies fall into the category of *community marketing* that provide opportunities to generate leads, set appointments, and advertise your business. Examples of community marketing include home and garden shows, partnerships with local hardware stores or retail stores, attending neighborhood block-parties, and even coordinating "solar home parties" with existing customers—any kind of event where you can set up a table or booth to generate interest in solar.

Community marketing can be expensive. For example, home and garden shows may charge a few thousand dollars for a booth, but they are generally the most effective because homeowners show up who are interested in home improvement. However, if paying to attend a home show is outside your company's budget—or your personal marketing budget—there are other affordable ways to grow your individual presence within the community. Like canvassing, which is an affordable and effective approach to taking your performance and skill development into your own hands, community marketing is often more effective than traditional marketing approaches—and more affordable.

Organizing your own events and partnerships within the community has the added benefit of developing recognition for you, your brand, and your business. Although some events may not be as fruitful as others, establishing your reputation in the community as the go-to person for solar ensures that when local homeowners want to know more, they reach out to you first. For example, attending a local block party in a suburban neighborhood may only put you in touch with five or six homeowners, but even generating one sale from a single event can prove to be a cost-effective form of marketing.

Like canvassing, community marketing and other types of field marketing result in personal interactions that leave stronger impressions with people who pave the way for future customers, referrals, and a more meaningful presence in the community. For local companies, this develops the reputation of a solid and trustworthy business. For a national company, the value is in establishing a greater local presence and connection with the market. Educating people about solar is rarely seen as out-of-character for community events that are typically designed to encourage togetherness, build relationships, and strengthen community values.

As an individual, there are many ways that you can create partnerships with local people, businesses, and organizations to build your personal brand within the community. Although corporate partnerships with companies that already have national recognition—Costco, Walmart, Home Depot, Lowe's, etc.—can be important to a company's competitive edge, establishing your own partnerships and attending community events on a smaller scale can certainly have an important role to play in your success. Here are three essential strategies for generating your own business through community marketing:

1. Build your brand within the community. Establish yourself as the authority for solar power, especially in neighborhoods and communities where you have the most customers. You will likely find yourself working in some neighborhoods and communities more than others. As you identify these communities, focus your efforts on building your brand and reputation as the local solar expert. This includes getting your business card or flyers in as many local businesses as possible, attending as many community events as possible, and simply becoming part of the community—as long as your interest in the community is genuine.

The best place to start is in *your* neighborhood because, naturally, you will spend the most time there. The more people who recognize you from local events, stores, and retail shops in the neighborhood—and other happenings in the community—the more likely they will be to come to you with their business or referrals. You can rely on your company to establish yourself as reliable and trustworthy, but building your own brand builds your reputation as somebody who is available to help your community members go solar.

2. Host solar parties for your customers. The importance of referrals is a common theme in the solar industry but making the most of them is not always easy. Every time you sign a customer up, you should be asking for referrals. They are not just to help you sell more solar but to help your customers save and earn more from solar. Even if your customer has a list of people they think might be interested in learning more about solar, they may not always be comfortable giving out contact information. Instead of leaving it to them, take it into your own hands by hosting a *solar home party*.

A solar home party is a simple event held at your customer's home. They invite their friends and family who might be candidates for solar, and you bring hors d'oeuvres and refreshments and give a short presentation on the benefits of going solar. There are two benefits to these events: First, your customer doesn't have to try and convince their contacts to go solar and potentially set the wrong expectations.

Second, even if the people you meet aren't qualified or interested, they may know other people who are and become referral sources themselves—and on it goes.

3. Build local partnerships. Many small business owners have a lot of stake in maintaining their business, which means they're probably interested in any opportunities to generate some additional revenue. Customers aren't the only ones who can generate referrals for you and make some extra cash, so establishing partnerships with local hardware stores, landscaping companies, roofers, and other businesses is an underutilized method for getting in touch with more homeowners.

Developing relationships with business owners and small businesses is often more effective and less time consuming than other marketing approaches. These strategies may not generate as much volume as canvassing or events, but establishing partnerships is the fastest way to increase your recognition and establish your reputation within the community. For example, you can offer a reward to business owners in exchange for putting up a flyer or poster, keeping a stack of business cards on the counter, or letting you set up a table on high-traffic shopping days. Each time you generate a lead or a sale, you can reward your local business owners for the partnership you have created.

The strategies outlined in this chapter are intended to help you generate more leads to sell more solar. After all, what's the point of reading this book if you have nobody to sell to? Following the Solar Sales

Method and employing the lead generation strategies in this chapter will help you generate more opportunities, but no matter how much you learn in this book, there is no substitute for experience.

You may only get a handful of leads from your company during your first few months as a solar sales consultant, which means you won't have as many opportunities to sell as you'd like. If you've still got your "training wheels" on, it may take some time to get the experience you need to develop good habits and improve your sales skills. If you settle for the leads you're given, it can take much longer to build your confidence and skills, which is possible to do through these other activities like canvassing and events.

Your first time canvassing is unlikely to produce a great number of leads—but by sticking with it and practicing, you will eventually build confidence and technique so you'll get at least one lead each time you go knock on doors. You may set up a table at your local hardware store a few times before you meet a homeowner interested in learning more. However, if you give up after the first try, you'll never make those extra sales. You may not always have to generate your own leads. On the other hand, you may find that generating your own leads is more fruitful and effective than company-generated leads. The purpose of this chapter is to provide the tools and techniques to create your own opportunities, in addition to those you are given by your employer.

The more you commit to developing deeper relationships with your customers, the more effective your sales approach will be. Becoming a top performer doesn't happen by sitting back and waiting for the opportunity to sell, and developing stronger sales skills won't happen by simply reading and studying sales techniques. The most successful sales professionals don't settle for what's given to them. They go out and make things happen, which allows them to develop their skills as fast as they're capable of improving. So, don't just settle for ten leads per week from your company. Get out and try to generate ten more using the strategies outlined in this chapter. If you're getting twenty leads per week from your company, what do you think will happen if you can get yourself twenty more leads each week? I'll give you a hint—if you're doubling the number of leads you get each week, you're also doubling your opportunities for sales, success, and income.

CHAPTER 15

BEFORE THE SELLING BEGINS

One of the most important ingredients for successful selling is preparation. If you're reading this book, you are getting ready to help future customers go solar. If you follow the Solar Sales Method, you will be preparing yourself and your customer for each step of the sales process and everything that comes afterwards. The better you understand your customer, the more prepared you will be to present their best option. And as you navigate each step along the way—from generating a new lead to signing a contract with your customer—there are many ways that you can set yourself up for success by simply being ready. So, how do you prepare to sell solar in the most effective way possible?

This chapter will show you how to deepen your connection with customers before and during each step of the Solar Sales Method. The following are small habits that go a long way toward positioning yourself to present the best possible solution—and being more successful even when you don't have time to prepare for everything. By now, you know that to sell solar effectively, you need to understand what you're selling, but more importantly, you need to know *who* you're working with.

The more prepared you are for your sales meeting, the more confidence your customer will have in you—not only because you demonstrate your knowledge of solar but also because you understand their needs, home, and financial situation. When you have all the information you need, you will be more prepared to present the best option. Before you start preparing for your sales appointment, there are two simple steps you can take to start in the right direction.

1. Introduction Phone Call or Pre-Qualification Call. Take any chance you can get to speak with your customer before you meet with them. The interview can begin well before your consultation with a customer (Chapter 8), and the sooner you get started, the better. Getting to know your customer before you meet with them can make a huge difference in the sales process. If you show up to your customer's home with no information, you'll have to spend a lot more time applying the material they give you to their solar solution. However, if you have already spoken to your customer in detail before your meeting, you can probably come up with a more accurate and appealing proposal and get to the solution in a shorter amount of time.

If you don't gather the information you need before your sales meeting, you will have a lot more work to do during your appointment, and you can end up wasting both you and your customer's time. Let your customer know what you need before your meeting—*"It would be helpful to speak for a few minutes before our meeting so I can get the information I need and learn a little more about you and what you're looking for."* Your customers are busy people, so be sure to make it clear that you're making an effort to save time—*"This phone call will save us a lot of time during our meeting."* Some customers prefer email or even text messaging over phone calls, so don't give up just because you didn't get a response to your voicemail.

The introduction phone call is about finding out as much as you can about your customer's personality, lifestyle, living situation, electric bills, and anything that might be relevant to your sales presentation—as well as their historical usage data if you haven't already gotten it. Here are some ideas of what to cover in the introduction phone call:

- **Why you're calling:** *"Hi, I am just about to start working on your solar proposal for our appointment on Tuesday, and I wanted to verify a few details. Is now a good time?"*
- **Setting Expectations:** *"Our meeting shouldn't take more than an hour; we'll discuss the benefits of solar and work together to find the perfect solution for your home."*
- **Pre-Interview Questions:** *"What are your primary goals for going solar?" "How long have you been thinking about going solar?" "What do you think you use the most electricity on?"*

The introduction call is important because speaking with your customers ahead of your meeting gives you a headstart on building a relationship with them. If you haven't spoken to the customer, you'll have to work harder to build a relationship while also preparing an attractive proposal during the same meeting. This also illustrates how generating your own leads—whether through canvassing, events, or referrals—provides a significant advantage by establishing a relationship between you and your customer from the very beginning.

2. Setting Expectations. No matter what part of the process you are in, preparing your customer for what comes next can do no harm. You have already learned the importance of setting expectations for your customer—from setting the agenda at the beginning of your sales meeting to explaining the "next steps" once your customer decides to go solar. You will become very familiar with the process of going solar but remember that your customers have probably never installed solar before, and likely have never looked into it, so part of your job will be making them feel comfortable and familiar each step of the way.

In the section above, setting expectations is suggested as part of the pre-qualification call. This doesn't mean you have to explain the entire process of going solar, but providing an overview of what to expect helps avoid surprises and, more importantly, can reinforce the decision to look into solar.

Setting expectations can include a broad view of the sales process, a brief description of the different financing options available, and even a summary of how solar works. Whatever subjects you cover before your sales meeting should focus on what your customer wants to know and what you need to know—*"What will happen during a solar consultation?" "How long will it take?" "What information should your customer have on hand for the meeting?"* Any questions your customer asks can be written down and addressed later—*"That's a great question, and I'll make sure to answer it for you during our meeting."*

Setting expectations is important for building trust, but the best way to affirm that trust is to follow through on your word. This can be a challenge, especially when you find yourself torn between providing too much information and not enough. One of the most difficult situations for solar sales professionals is when a customer says, *"I don't want to meet you unless I know the price."*

The truth is that it is virtually impossible to estimate the price of a solar project and the benefits it creates without first putting together a proposal. You always want to make sure your customer understands that the benefits of solar outweigh the costs before you present the price (Chapter 11). However, creating an accurate proposal is not possible until you have gathered some specific data from the customer. Even then, many factors can affect the cost and benefits. Nevertheless, you will inevitably meet many customers who want to know the "ballpark price" before they meet with you. Telling them, *"I know price is important to you, but before I can tell you how much this will cost, there is some other information that I need from you,"* doesn't always work.

Here are a couple simple ways to respond to price questions without scaring away your customers—or sounding like you're hiding something.

Techniques for Ballpark Pricing

#1: The Redirect: When a customer asks, *"How much?"* they probably already have a big number in their head. They are either hoping you'll give them a much lower price than that, or they're anticipating your response and preparing to say, *"That's more than I can afford right now."* The bottom line is that solar is a big investment, and overestimating or underestimating your ballpark price may end up hurting your chances of closing a sale. Until your customer understands *why* the price of solar is so high, and *what* the benefits are, they're unlikely to want to go any further discussing solar with you. One way to prepare the customer for the cost of solar is to redirect their question with some quick math.

You might begin your response with, *"I know price is important, but I'd have to put together a quote before I can provide you with an accurate number."* But the customer is still hoping for an answer, so you ask what their average electric bill is. For example, let's say they spend $110 per month. First, multiply this number by twelve months ($1,320), then by twenty years ($26,400), and you have another big number to put in the customer's head: *the cost of doing nothing.* Now, the question you can pose to your customer is, *"How much would you be willing to invest to avoid paying that much money to your utility company?"*

What's more, this ballpark cost doesn't account for the rising cost of electricity and other ways utilities are increasing their customer's rates, such as tiered and time-of-use rates. The actual cost of going solar may be 20 percent *less* than what they're currently paying, or it could be 20 percent *more*. It all depends on the market they live in and what incentives are available, if any. The fact is that by going solar, your customers will begin saving money, not spending more of it, and you must be able to communicate this message with your ballpark calculations.

If your customer doesn't have a problem spending tens of thousands of dollars on electricity, you're likely in for a tough sell. However, if you can sell your customer on the possibility of saving even *more,* so they agree to take a look at a customized solution, you're one step closer to closing the sale.

#2: The Averages. Another way to prepare customers for the cost of going solar with a ballpark figure is by explaining average costs and savings for solar costumers in their market—or in the United States as a whole. You can find the average cost of going solar from data in your company's CRM or from nationwide industry data. However, ballparking average savings is more difficult and may require you to keep track of how much money you are saving each of your customers.

The average cost of going solar for homeowners in the United States is around $16,000—*before* the federal ITC is applied. However, this number can be deceiving as prices can range from as little as $6,000 to well over $50,000 depending on several factors (the biggest determination being the size of the solar installation). Costs vary greatly depending on the maturity of the market, levels of competition, local electricity prices, and the quality of equipment being used, among other factors. In some cases, describing this broad price range is enough for the customer to recognize that receiving a customized quote is the only way to answer their question—*"The average cost of going solar before incentives is between $10,000 and $22,000 in the U.S., so if you really want to know how much solar will cost, I'll have to put together a custom quote for you."*

Estimating the average cost of solar is relatively straightforward, but calculating the saving and benefits is a little more complicated. Furthermore, customers will often ask what price they should expect, but they will rarely ask how much they can save. Instead of focusing on price and telling your customer what they think they need to know, take this opportunity to tell them something *you* want them to know: their potential savings.

Solar customers in the United States can save between $10,000 and $30,000 *on average*, but determining savings is very much dependent on the market you are in. For example, the average price of a 6 kW solar installation in Washington is around $12,000, so solar can save around $14,000 over the lifetime of the system (because electricity in the region is supplied by low-cost hydropower). In comparison, the same 6 kW system would cost around $14,000 in Massachusetts, but lifetime savings exceed $45,000 (because of attractive incentives and a much higher cost of electricity).

Qualified homeowners who invest in solar will eventually save money, without a doubt. Unfortunately, "how much" and "how quickly" is often a more decisive factor. It is always best to save the price talk for your solar consultation, but at the very least, discussing average costs and savings sets some expectations for your customer without scaring them away. At best, it will get them excited to find out if their savings will fall on the higher end of the spectrum.

Whether you are gathering information about your customer, explaining what lies ahead, mitigating concerns about astronomical price tags, or indulging in the possibility of saving a boatload of money, the process of selling solar starts well before the actual consultation. The more you can accomplish *before* you start selling, the more time and energy you will ultimately save for both you and your customer.

The purpose of this chapter is to reiterate the importance of preparation, both for you and your customers. The strategies above are intended to help navigate the pre-sales process. Everything you do leading up to a sales meeting will impact your ability to perform the subsequent steps of the Solar Sales Method. As you prepare for your next sales meeting, begin incorporating the lessons you have learned in this book. With practice and experience, it will become second nature.

CHAPTER 16

PUTTING IT ALL TOGETHER

The Solar Sales Method, along with these strategies, tips, and tricks, do not amount to a "secret recipe" that will automatically set you apart from your colleagues. Simply reading this book is no guarantee that your performance will improve. However, with experience and practice employing the methods outlined above, you can sell with more clarity, confidence, and overall effectiveness. Two of the most important factors for more effective selling are consistency and preparedness, both of which are entrenched in the methods provided in this book.

At some point, you might have found yourself thinking, *"If my competitors are reading this book, too, how is it going to help me?"*

The answer is summed up by a common adage in the solar industry: *a rising tide lifts all boats.* The purpose here is not to train a small number of super-performers, but to instead instill more consistency in the selling practices used throughout the residential solar industry. The landscape of solar sales is quite varied today. Any given homeowner looking into solar is likely to see completely different designs, prices, savings, and production estimates in each quote they receive. Ultimately, this inconsistency does little for the progress of the solar industry as a whole.

As long as solar remains a highly customized product, it will continue to fall on the shoulders of sales consultants to design and present solutions to their customers. As competition in the residential solar market grows, the "race to the bottom" (vying for the lowest price) actually makes it *more* difficult to sell the best solution to customers at the right price—to sell solar with integrity. More solar companies are looking for ways to stand out by offering lower prices, system adders, or other gimmicks to attract customers, all of which is making it more difficult to sell solar for what it is: a cost-effective alternative to paying utility bills.

The Solar Sales Method strives to embody the future of the solar industry. A future in which customers aren't confused by vastly different designs, production estimates, and prices. A future in which customers confidently choose to work with the company they trust—and salespeople they feel most connected to—rather than feeling the need to choose the lowest price. A future in which customers are not discouraged from going solar because each quote they receive looks completely different and they don't know who or what to believe. Professionals who follow the Solar Sales Method, or employ a similar sales strategy that prioritizes honesty, accuracy, and integrity over price and close ratios, are building the future of the solar industry.

TAKE CONTROL OF YOUR SALES PROCESS

By the time you finish this book, you will be a self-certified solar sales professional who can approach customers confidently—knowing what to say and how to say it. You know who to help and how to help them. If you're applying for jobs in solar sales, you'll be more prepared for your interviews. If you're beginning a career in solar sales, you are ready to hit the ground running. If you're already in solar sales, you can apply these new lessons and methods to take your performance to the next level. Whatever your situation, you're ready to put everything you've learned in this book together to sell more solar, more effectively.

No matter what stage of your solar sales career you are in, you will continue to learn more about solar technology, policy, and the industry as a whole—the "solar coaster" will continue its ups and downs. Your goal should never be "peak performance" because there are always new skills to employ, new tools to learn, and new ways to push yourself above and beyond. New tools are regularly introduced in the solar industry, from design and proposal software to solar production calculators to general information websites and blogs. The more effort you put into adapting and growing along with the industry, the more likely your performance will follow the same pattern of growth.

The Solar Sales Method is focused on the experience you provide to your customer, but your success also depends on your command of the tools that your company provides. For example, in most cases, the design and proposal tools will have limited control over variables that affect the proposals you create for customers. Employing the Solar Sales Method encourages you to focus on mastering your process, which will help you maintain control of the entire sales process no matter who you're working with. Similarly, consistent practice and experience with the tools you are provided are essential for staying focused and on track even when you cannot control all of the outcomes of your proposals.

CLARIFY YOUR PERSONAL MISSION AND VISION

Many companies have mission and vision statements designed to communicate core values and beliefs that drive the business. These statements play an important role in providing customers with a clear and concise understanding of what the company is "all about," and help it stand out from the competition. Mission and vision statements are also useful guides toward more meaningful presentations and conversations with customers. However, strong mission and vision statements are not only important for a company's success; they're also important for *you* to clarify your values as a solar sales professional.

In practice, mission and vision statements are useful for advertising and selling products so that customers understand and connect with them. These statements explain what companies care about, or even what they actually *do*, but they also attract employees. As you seek out an employer, you may find yourself drawn to their mission or vision, but not all companies have these clear statements. Regardless of whether the company you work for has a mission and vision statement, creating your own will give you something to remind you of your own purpose and approach to selling solar.

Just as you go through the exercise of writing down a few paragraphs about your story to demonstrate yourself to customers (Chapter 9), preparing a personal vision and mission statement can help you stay on track towards meeting your own goals. As you approach the end of this book, take the time to write down the things that motivate you, inspire you to help your customers, and encapsulate your purpose as a solar sales professional. As an individual, creating your personal mission and vision statement is an exercise that can help you clarify what is important to you and your business.

PUTTING IT ALL TOGETHER

As you grow a career in solar sales, this book will serve as a guide to what matters most. This includes helping you focus your attention in the right places during the sales process and learning how to get to know your customers better so you can present more attractive solutions. In addition to developing more effective sales skills and strategies, this book is also a reminder to focus on what motivates you—what drives you to achieve *your own goals*.

There is no better way to achieving your goals than to write them down and return to them over and over. Another thing to keep in mind as you come up with personal goals is to set yourself up for success by giving yourself the chance to succeed. If your goal is to sell twenty-five deals in your first month, this is not impossible, but it is unreasonable to set yourself up with such a monumental goal right off the bat. Instead, give yourself a chance to set your sights ever higher by setting smaller, more reasonable goals to build momentum. Write down a handful of small goals, return to them each day, each week, and each month, and soon you will find yourself crossing off the items on your list. This is not to say that you shouldn't give yourself ambitious targets, but taking many small steps is just as effective as making fewer big leaps.

The same goes for reading this book. As you reach the end, you cannot expect to have digested everything and fully prepared yourself for a successful career in solar sales. To make the most of this book and the strategies within, apply what you have learned and then return to it again when you have had some practice and experience applying the Solar Sales Method. Each time you return to it, you will find a new strategy to apply, and eventually, it will all come together. By reading this book, you have already achieved one goal, taking a step towards cultivating a more successful career in solar sales and improving your performance. You can cross that goal off your list.

GLOSSARY

Alternating Current (AC): *A common type of electric current used to power homes and businesses that reverses its direction at regularly recurring intervals when traveling through a conductor.*

American Recovery and Reinvestment Act of 2009 (Recovery Act): *A federal stimulus bill passed in 2009 that scaled up investment in renewable energy and authorized the uncapped 30 percent Solar Investment Tax Credit.*

Avoided Cost of Power: *The price customers avoid paying to their utility company by going solar, calculated by finding the difference between how much a customer would pay for electricity from the utility and how much a customer would pay for solar over the lifetime of their solar PV system.*

Central Inverter: See *Inverter*

Change Order: *A document used to communicate amendments to a solar contract providing a revised scope of work, new pricing, and other relevant modifications for approval from the customer. It often requires the signatures of both the contractor and the customer.*

Conductor: *An object or type of material that allows the flow of an electric current in one or more directions, such as the copper wire in transmission and distribution lines.*

Cost per Acquisition: *A measurement of the total amount of expenses incurred by an entity to acquire a new customer, including all expenses from advertising to the closed sale.*

Delivery Charges: *A category of charges imposed by utility companies that cover the costs associated with delivering electricity to customers, including distribution, transmission, grid maintenance, and other operating expenses.*

Demand Charges: *An increasingly common billing structure imposed by utility companies that is calculated by determining the maximum amount of electricity a customer uses at one time during the billing cycle.*

Direct Current (DC): *The type of electric current produced by solar panels; an electric current that flows in one direction through a conductor, typically at low voltage and high current.*

Distribution: *The final stage of the electrical grid, made up of utility poles, power lines, and transformers that provide low-voltage electricity to the homes and businesses of consumers connected to the grid.*

Distributed Energy Resource (DER): *A category of technologies that supply electricity to the electric grid at the distribution level, including power generation, energy management, and storage systems that can be used to improve the operation of the energy system.*

Economy of Scale: *Cost advantages achieved when an increasing level of demand and production allow for a reduction in the cost-per-unit output of a product or service.*

Electric Bill Savings: *The amount of money in dollar terms that a customer is able to save by going solar, calculated simply by finding the difference of customers utility bill before solar and their utility bill after solar.*

Electric Grid: *The integrated network of power generation facilities, transmission networks, and distribution networks that make up a power supply system providing electricity to customers over a large area.*

Electric Meter: *A device that measures the amount of electricity produced or consumed by a home or business, used by utility companies for monitoring and billing purposes.*

Electricity Charges: *A category of charges imposed by utility companies that cover the costs associated with producing electricity at power generation facilities that is delivered to customers for consumption through the electric grid.*

Energy Policy Act of 1992: *The last federal energy legislation of the twentieth century establishing renewable energy incentives and making the 10 percent commercial investment tax credit permanent.*

Energy Policy Act of 2005 (EPAct): *The first energy legislation of the twenty-first century that extended the scope of federal renewable energy incentives and re-established the investment tax credit for residential solar energy systems.*

Energy Tax Act of 1978: *A federal legislation that established the investment tax credit for residential solar investments at 30 percent of the first $2,000 and 20 percent of the next $8,000, in* *addition to the 10 percent investment tax credit available on all types of solar equipment.*

Equipment Warranties: *The category of warranties provided by solar power equipment manufacturers that guarantee protection from functional defects, environmental issues, and premature wear and tear of solar equipment.*

Feed-In-Tariff (FIT): *A category of incentives that offers a long-term contract to renewable energy producers and compensates the owner of a generation facility with payments of above-market prices for electricity supplied to the electric grid.*

Field Marketing: *A type of direct marketing that involves employees prospecting and promoting solar power in the field, typically through canvassing, events, retail sales, and other face-to-face communication methods.*

Generation: *The initial stage of the electric grid, where electricity is produced by power generation facilities, typically large-scale, centralized fossil fuel power plants that deliver high-voltage electricity to transmission power lines.*

Greenhouse Gas Emissions: *Any gases that have the property of absorbing heat energy radiating from Earth's surface, most commonly carbon dioxide and methane that are emitted during the process of burning fossil fuels in conventional power generation facilities.*

Grid-Connected PV System: *A solar photovoltaic system that is interconnected to the utility grid so that it may act as a distributed generation facility delivering excess electricity to the electric grid.*

Hard Costs: *Hardware-related costs associated with photovoltaic solar installations that are predictable and quantifiable, including the cost of solar modules, inverters, racking, and other equipment.*

Historical Usage: *The amount of electricity consumed by utility customers over an extended period of time, typically twelve months, used by solar companies to accurately size solar solutions.*

Inside Sales: *A discipline of sales and marketing that takes place remotely by professionals who reach out to customers and perform consultations for products and services over the phone or virtually.*

Interconnection: *The technical process of a utility company allowing a distributed generation facility to connect to the electric grid, typically initiated by a solar company on behalf of the customer.*

Inverter: *A device that converts direct current (DC) electricity generated by solar modules into alternating current (AC) electricity that can be used in homes and businesses or supplied to the electric grid.*

Investment Tax Credit (ITC): *A federal tax incentive that provides an income tax credit to qualified solar power investments.*

Islanding Effect: *A situation that occurs when a grid-connected distributed generation facility continues to produce power while the electric grid is down, creating a dangerous situation for utility workers who may not realize the circuit is still powered.*

Kilowatt-Hour (kWh): *A standard unity of electrical power equal to 1,000 watts consumed over the course of one hour.*

Lifecycle Emissions: *The estimated emissions that result from manufacturing, owning, and operating a photovoltaic system over the period of its useful life.*

Lifecycle Impacts: *The estimated environmental impacts caused by manufacturing, owning, and operating a photovoltaic system over the period of its useful life.*

Load: *An entity that consumes energy and creates demand on an energy-producing system.*

Megawatt (MW): *A unit of electrical power equal to 1,000 kilowatts or 1 million watts, a standard measure of electric power plant generating capacity.*

Micro-Inverter: *A device that converts direct current (DC) electricity generated by a single solar module into alternating current (AC) electricity that can be combined with multiple inverters and solar modules for use in homes and businesses or supply to the electric grid.*

Mission Statement: *A short statement defining the culture, values, ethics, and fundamental goals describing the overall purpose of an organization.*

Net Investment: *The total amount of money a customer initially spends on an investment in solar, minus the savings and tax credits provided from that investment.*

Net Meter: *A secondary electric meter installed by the utility company for grid-connected solar PV installations that measures how much power the customer supplies back to the grid and is used for net metering billing purposes.*

Net Metering: *A utility billing mechanism that allows residential and commercial customers who generate electricity from solar to supply excess electricity back to the grid. They are then only billed for their "net" energy use.*

Net Metering Bank: *A bank of excess electricity credited to a net-metered customer who generates more electricity than their home uses during daylight that can be used at night or when their electricity use exceeds their system's output.*

Outside Sales: *A discipline of sales and marketing that takes place outside traditional offices by professionals who present their products and services to customers through face-to-face interactions.*

Offset: *The portion of a customer's electric bill that is replaced by solar power production.*

One-Call Close: *A desirable outcome in sales in which a customer and sales professional complete a sale during the initial sales meeting, shortening the sales cycle and increasing close rates.*

One-Line Diagram: *A simplified document representing all electrical elements and necessary equipment for interconnection of a power system, also called a single-line diagram.*

Payback Period: *The amount of time it takes for an investor to break even or recover the cost of their net investment.*

Photon: *A particle of light that acts as an individual unit of energy.*

Photovoltaic Cell (PV Cell): *A single element of a solar electric module that performs the immediate conversion of light into electrical energy using the photovoltaic effect.*

Photovoltaic Effect (PV Effect): *The phenomenon that occurs when particles of light displace electrons in certain materials, causing an electrical charge that can be carried by a semiconductor.*

Photovoltaic Module (PV Module): *A collection of photovoltaic solar cells mounted in a framework that is used to generate direct current electricity from sunlight, commonly called a solar panel.*

Photovoltaic System (PV System): *A complete and connected electrical system made up of multiple solar modules, inverters, racking, and necessary equipment that converts sunlight into electricity.*

Pitch Book: *A collection of sales materials organized in a deliberate way to facilitate an effective presentation to customers interested in going solar.*

Power Plants: *Large, centralized power production facilities where electricity generation takes place, typically from the combustion of fossil fuels, but also including nuclear power, hydropower, and renewable energy sources.*

Power Purchase Agreement (PPA): *A contract used in the energy industry in which an electricity consumer agrees to purchase stable and low-cost electricity from a third-party owner and operator of a generation facility.*

Positive Externalities: *A beneficial result from a purchase or investment that is not specifically agreed upon and often unintentional.*

Price Adders: *Additional costs necessary for completing a safe and high-quality solar installation, typically calculated as a per-watt price or a fixed dollar amount.*

Production-Based Incentive (PBI): *A financial incentive paid to the owner of a solar power facility based on the amount of electricity generated.*

Production Estimates: *The amount of electricity that solar companies estimate a solar PV system will generate by taking into account the specifications of the system as well as weather, shade, and other factors that affect production.*

Production Guarantee: *A guarantee offered by some solar companies in which a customer is reimbursed for underperformance or repair of equipment under warranty to ensure a guaranteed level of production.*

Production Warrantee: *A category of warranties offered by solar panel manufacturers that ensure a certain level of performance and reliability from solar panels and equipment over a period of ten to twenty-five years.*

Project Manager: *The individual responsible for planning, organization, and communication with solar customers from the time a contract is signed throughout the installation process until completing the project.*

Proposal Tool: *A type of software used by solar professionals to create designs, proposals, and contracts for solar PV systems to improve efficiency and streamline the sales process across organizations.*

Public Utilities Regulatory Policy Act (PURPA): *A federal policy passed in 1978 promoting energy efficiency and renewable energy development that enabled net metering and distributed generation resources in the solar power industry.*

PVWatts: *The standard tool used in the solar industry to calculate production estimates for grid-connected solar PV systems, developed by the National Renewable Energy Laboratory (NREL)*

Qualified Lead: *A prospective customer who has indicated an interest in going solar and meets the minimum requirements for going solar based on their home, financial standing, and electricity consumption.*

Rate of Return: *The rate at which a customer's investment in solar is recouped.*

Referral Program: *An incentive program organized by a solar company that rewards participants for successfully referring potential customers to the organization.*

Residential Solar: *A category of solar energy systems installed on residential properties that converts sunlight to meet the home's electricity needs.*

Retail Rate: *The total price per kilowatt-hour charged by utility companies including all costs of service, generation, and delivery.*

Rooftop Solar: *A category of solar energy systems installed on the rooftop of homes and businesses to provide on-site electricity to the building.*

The Sales Cycle: *The series of events that takes place from the first interaction between a salesperson and a prospective customer up until the point the sale is consummated.*

Sales Lead: *A prospective customer who expresses interest in a product or service.*

Sales Pipeline: *A collection of sales leads and potential customers that is often used to forecast how many customers a salesperson has the potential to close within a certain time frame or to estimate the potential to meet a sales quota.*

Semiconductor: *A material with a limited capacity to conduct an electric current that is used in the photovoltaic conversion process.*

Silica Oxide (SiO2): *A semi-metallic chemical element commonly found in sand that serves as the primary semiconductor in solar photovoltaic devices.*

Silicon Wafers: *A thin slice of solid crystalline silicon used to manufacture solar cells.*

Soft Close: *A sales technique that prepares the customer to purchase a product or service without the pressure of closing the sale.*

Soft Costs: *Non-hardware costs related to PV systems, such as financing, permitting, installation, interconnection, and inspection that are often more difficult to predict.*

Solar-as-a-Service: See *Third-Party Ownership*

Solar Access: *A customer's ability to receive sunlight on their property without obstruction from another person or entity's property, including buildings, foliage, or other impediments.*

Solar Array: *See Photovoltaic System*

Solar Consultation: *The meeting between a solar sales professional and a prospective customer to discuss the details and costs associated with the transaction to go solar.*

Solar Electric Systems: *A category of solar technology that results in the production of electricity from sunlight to supply electricity to homes and businesses.*

Solar Electric Module: See *Photovoltaic Module*

Solar Energy Systems: Technology that converts energy from sunlight into useful energy sources, including heat, electric, and mechanical energy.

Solar Investment Tax Credit (ITC): *See Investment Tax Credit.*

Solar Thermal Systems: A category of solar technology that harnesses heat energy from the sun for use in residential and commercial applications.

Solar Panel: *See Photovoltaic Module*

Solar Cell: *See Photovoltaic Cell*

Solar Loan: *A financing mechanism in which a homeowner borrows money from a lender to finance a solar installation and pays it back with interest through monthly installations over a period of time.*

Solar Lease: *A financing mechanism of third-party ownership in which a homeowner receives the benefits of a solar system without purchasing or taking ownership of the equipment and pays monthly installations over a period of time.*

Solar Home Party: *A marketing event organized by a solar sales professional and hosted at the home of an existing solar customer intended to generate referrals for residential solar sales.*

Solar Proposal: *A collection of documents generated by a solar sales professional that describes a customer's solar installation, including the design, production estimates, price, and other important factors needed in the decision-making process.*

Solar Service Company: *A company that maintains third-party ownership of a solar electric system installed on the property of a customer in exchange for monthly payments*

String Inverter: *See Inverter*

Third-Party Ownership (TPO): *A financing mechanism in which a homeowner agrees to purchase stable and low-cost electricity from a third-party owner and operator of a solar PV system installed on their property.*

Tiered Rates: *A utility rate structure in which the cost of electricity* *increases when more electricity is consumed, typically when a certain amount of power is exceeded.*

Transmission: *The stage of the electric grid made up of high-voltage power lines that carry electricity from centralized power plants to distribution networks that supply homes and businesses with electricity.*

Turnkey Installation: *A fully operational solar PV system completed by a solar company on behalf of their customer, including design, installation, and commissioning services.*

Tariffs: *A collection of electric charges that is used to calculate the retail rates that utility companies use for billing purposes.*

Usage: *The consumption of electricity by a household or business monitored over a certain period of time and used for billing purposes*

Utility-Scale Solar: *A sector of the solar industry that is made up of large-scale solar projects that supply wholesale electricity to the electric grid.*

Utility Service Fee: *An unavoidable charge imposed by utility companies that solar customers continue to pay in exchange for remaining grid-connected and benefiting from net metering.*

Workmanship Warranty: *A category of warranties that provides coverage against any errors that occur during installation by a solar company, typically five to ten years after installation.*

Wholesale Rate: *The cost of electricity sold by power producers participating in the sale of electricity on the wholesale market, such as the electricity generated at a power plant that is supplied to the utility grid.*

APPENDIX A

SAMPLE CUSTOMER ACCOUNT WORKSHEET

CUSTOMER NAME: *Ray Franklin*

FAMILY MEMBER(S): *Elizabeth (Wife), Devin (son, 12), Beth (daughter, 9)*

ADDRESS: *2289 South Sunshine Drive*

CITY: *Richmond*

UTILITY COMPANY: *Big Burn Electric*

AVG. BILL: *~$200* (HIGH BILL: *$380* LOW BILL: *$130*)

OTHER NOTES: *Original roof, 3 years old, house built in 2017. No shade now, one small oak growing in back yard*

CUSTOMER ACCOUNT WORKSHEET

Customer Details:______________________________

Customer Information: (The Interview)________________

(On-Topic Questions)

- *Neighbors told them about their experience, want to find out their options, bills are high enough to consider other options. (What made you look into solar?)*

- *Since they moved in, electric bills have been up and down. Just started looking into solar. Haven't gotten a quote before. (How long have you been considering solar?)*

- *Electric usage from TV & computers. Devin's video games, Beth's TV shows. Lights, appliances, central A/C in summer. (Where do you use most electricity?)*

(Off-Topic Questions)

- *Moved into the neighborhood from across town last year, wanted better schools and to be closer to Ray's work (engineer). (How long have you lived in your home?)*
- *Ray is an engineer (and pilot!) at a commercial construction outfit. Elizabeth is in advertising. Kids are self-sufficient and have after-school sports. (What kind of work do you do?)*
- *Elizabeth's parents live nearby, help with the kids and activities so R & E can manage to work full time. (How do you balance your busy schedules?)*
- *Both are into bicycling, hiking, camping. (What do you do in your free time?)*

Customer Questions:

- *How much are we paying for electricity right now?*
- *How do we apply for the Federal Tax Credit?*
- *What if they want to pay cash?*
- *How long will they need to make loan payments?*
- *What if something breaks?*
- *What happens when they move?*

Customer Motivations:

- *Want to join neighborhood trend, be part of the solution (environmentally conscious)*
- *Interested in taking advantage of tax credit before it expires*
- *Would like to spend less on electricity, if possible*
- *Save up for a family trip to Spain one summer*

ACKNOWLEDGMENTS

Much of what I know about solar, I learned from hands-on experience and by working with exceptional people. This book could not possibly include all the lessons I have learned from my colleagues, managers, and customers, nor could it include all of the insight I have gained while working with them.

Among the many people I have to thank are Eric Doub, who gave me my first job in the field of sustainability as a jack-of-all-trades at his zero-energy home business, teaching me about project coordination, construction, finance, and the nuances of management. Sam Sours and Eric Blank, who provided my first internship in solar and later hired me to support utility-scale solar projects, giving me hands-on experience with renewable energy policy and project development. TJ Slocum, who gave me my first job in residential solar when I finished grad school. Brian Sharpe, not only a friend but a mentor who, after promoting me to a leadership role, showed me how to be an effective manager and taught me the importance of earning the trust and respect of others. And Jason Little, who showed me I could push myself further than I thought possible. He sadly passed away before I could let him know how much I learned from him and how much he inspired me.

I also must thank my professors and community members at the University of Colorado at Boulder and the University of Denver. They were instrumental in helping me discover environmentalism and find my career path in the solar power industry. Thank you to Dave Newport, Dale Miller, Paul Komor, Tom Yulsman, Dr. Anita Halvorssen, K.K. DuVivier, Marianne Martin, Dana Kelly, and Tricia Dinkel.

My family, friends, and colleagues have taught me many of the lessons in this book, helped me become a better manager, and inspired me to complete this book. While I can't name them all, among them are Julia Winton, Sam Johnson, Erik Bruner, Jordan Tallman, John Bumgarner, Henry Nagy, Jason Menchen, Shane Scott, Kelly Gu, Melissa Segil, Joe Boccardo, Shayna Omeara, Garrett Pitcher, Scott Daigle, Michael Fitzpatrick, Grace Brown, Thierry van der Star, Kayla Andis, Ellen Jones, Stephan Kim, and Tom Brown. Finally, thank you to my parents and my sister, Robin, who have supported me through the process of writing this book and kept me on track.

To all the others I have worked with and can't mention here, as well as the many more I will meet in the future, our mission goes beyond generating clean power and conserving natural resources. Together, we are creating a future that we can be proud of.

ABOUT THE AUTHOR

Daniel Howson is a proven leader in the solar power industry with over ten years of experience in sales, field marketing, management, training, and market development. He has recruited, trained, and managed field marketing and sales professionals, helping launch and develop careers in the renewable energy industry. His work has contributed to over $9.5 million in revenue and more than 2.48 megawatts of installed residential solar energy capacity.

Since 2014, Daniel has been developing comprehensive training curriculums and materials that teach field marketing and sales skills to industry professionals. His mission is to help educate solar energy professionals through his publications, providing a framework for training and development in the solar industry based on high-integrity, honest, and effective sales.

To explore sales training or consulting possibilities for your organization, please contact Daniel Howson via his website at SellingSolar.net or email him at Daniel@sellingsolar.net.

Quantity discounts are available for this book. Please inquire for more information.

Made in United States
Orlando, FL
15 June 2022